CONTENTS

Everyone knows what a knight is...

IT'S WHEN IT'S DARK, INNIT
THAT IS SO-O-O INTERESTING I AM ALMOST STAYING AWAKE

OF COURSE YOU MUSTN'T MIX IT UP WITH THE WORD 'NIGHT' ... THE OPPOSITE OF 'DAY'. THAT LEADS TO A LOT OF VERY BAD JOKES ABOUT HAVING A KNIGHT OFF, KNIGHT SCHOOLS AND KNIGHT-MARES.
YOU'RE PROBABLY WONDERING WHY 'KNIGHT' - THE SOLDIER ON A HORSE - IS SPELLED WITH A K? WELL, HERE'S AN INTERESTING THING ... IN THE MIDDLE AGES THEY USED TO SAY THE LETTER 'K', SO A SOLDIER ON A HORSE WAS A 'KER-NIGHT'.

YOU ARE RIGHT. YOU DON'T WANT TO HEAR FRUMPY FACTS ABOUT THESE BATTLING BULLIES. YOU WANT TO HEAR TALES OF TERROR, CHARGING AND CHOPPING, SLICING AND SWORD-PLAY, MASHING WITH MACES, PRINCESSES IN PERIL AND DEALING DEATH TO DRAGONS.

ROAR!

CLANK

SMACK

YEAH. BLOOD ON EVERY PAGE PLEASE

I CAN'T PROMISE BLOOD ON EVERY PAGE BECAUSE YOU'D GET IT ALL OVER YOUR HANDS AND IT WOULD DRIP INTO YOUR PORRIDGE ... IF YOU READ BOOKS AT BREAKFAST, THAT IS.

BUT LET'S CUT OUT THE STODGY STUFF, AND RIDE THROUGH HISTORY LIKE RICHARD III ON HIS GREAT WHITE CHARGER. (EXCEPT RICHARD III DIED AT THE END OF HIS CHARGE AND MOST HORRIBLE HISTORIES READERS MANAGE TO SURVIVE. BUT YOU KNOW WHAT I MEAN.)

LET'S HAVE A HIGH-SPEED HISTORY OF KNIGHTS. YES ... IT'S KNIGHT TIME!

ROLAND'S ROTTEN END

15 AUGUST, AD 778

WHAT IS A KNIGHT? IT'S A NOBLE MAN ON A HORSE, WHOSE JOB IS TO KILL HIS ENEMIES. BUT IT IS MORE THAN THAT. THE KNIGHT HAS 'RULES' CALLED CHIVALRY. CHIVALRY MEANS HE CAN DO DAFT THINGS ... LIKE FIGHT TO THE DEATH TO SAVE HIS FRIENDS. WHERE DID THESE 'RULES' COME FROM? FROM STORIES. TRUE TALES OF HEROES OR MADE-UP TALES. OTHER KNIGHTS HEARD THE STORIES THEN SAID, 'OOOOH! THAT'S WHAT WE SHOULD BE DOING.' STORIES ABOUT KNIGHTS LIKE ROLAND...

KING CHARLES THE GREAT OF FRANCE (SOMETIMES CALLED CHARLEMAGNE) WAS ... GREAT.
I'M GREAT, I AM. ME AND MY KNIGHTS ARE UNBEATABLE. KNIGHTS LIKE ROLAND HERE
ME, AND MY TRUSTY SWORD CALLED DURENDAL
I'M A LORD'S SWORD - A CUT ABOVE THE REST
NOT TO MENTION MY FAITHFUL HORSE, VEILLANTIF
I'M THE MANE REASO
FOR HIS SUCCESS
HUH! ROLAND SAID NOT TO MENTION YOU

THINK YOU ARE FORGETTING MENTION ME ... YOUR LOYAL FRIEND OLIVER
OH, YES ... AND WHATSISNAME. JOLLY OLLY
DON'T FORGET IT WAS WITH MY HELP, YOU CHEEKY CHARLIE
I, CHARLES THE GREAT, SMASHED THE SAXONS ... WITH ROLAND'S HELP
AND MINE!
AND I HAD A HOOF IN IT TOO
BUT WHEN WE INVADED SPAIN IT WAS A LOT TOUGHER...
...HE MEANS WE LOST

NO, NO! WE JUST SORT OF ... DIDN'T WIN
BUT YOU CAPTURED LOTS OF LOVELY LOOT, MY NOBLE KING
AS IF A HEAVY HORSEMAN AND HIS SWORD WASN'T ENOUGH TO CARRY? BAGS OF GOLD TOO
WE REACHED A HIGH MOUNTAIN PASS ON THE ROAD BACK TO FRANCE...
HEAVY HORSEMAN, SWORD, BAGS OF GOLD AND MOUNTAINS TO CLIMB!
WHINNY, WHINNY, WHINGE - THAT'S ALL YOU EVER DO
AND THAT'S WHERE WE RAN INTO TROUBLE...
WE ARE IN THE LAND OF THE BASQUES, MY LORD. DANGEROUS FIGHTERS
BIG BAD BASQUES MAKE OLLY LESS JOLLY

THE FORESTS ARE THICK AND THE PATHS ARE NARROW
THEY ARE ALSO STEEP AND STONY, BUT DO THEY THINK ABOUT ME AND MY HOOVES? NO!
WE WILL HAVE TO TRAVEL IN A LINE. THE BASQUES COULD ATTACK FROM THE TREES WHILE WE'RE STRUNG OUT
STRUNG UP? I DON'T WANT TO BE STRUNG UP!
THEY WON'T ATTACK THE FRONT OF OUR ARMY. THEY WOULD BE SLAUGHTERED BY THE REST
IN THAT CASE I'LL GO AT THE FRONT!
SO I WILL TRAVEL AT THE FRONT
OH, BUMS
AND WE WILL TRAVEL AT THE BACK TO GUARD YOUR REAR
IT'S ROLAND'S FAT REAR THAT BOTHERS ME. WHAT A WEIGHT!

AND SO THE FRENCH ARMY STARTED TO MARCH THROUGH THE PASS.
BRAVE AND LOYAL ROLAND. BLOW THIS ELEPHANT HORN IF YOU ARE ATTACKED. WE'LL COME BACK AND SAVE YOU
ELEPHANT HORNS TO CARRY NOW. WHY CAN'T HE JUST WHISTLE?
SURE ENOUGH, THE BASQUES ATTACKED ROLAND'S REAR GUARD...
DEATH TO THE STINKING FRENCH
YEAH, THE FRENCH HAVE A STENCH
BLOW THE HORN, OLIVER!
OUCH!
NO NEED. A NOBLE KNIGHT IS NOT AFRAID OF A SPANISH ARMY
HOOF

BUT THERE ARE FIVE SPANISH ARMIES ATTACKING. BLOW THE BLEEDING HORN YOU NITWIT, NOBLE NUMBSKULL
MY SWORD WILL RUN WITH SPANISH BLOOD...
UGH. STICKY AND WARM. I CAN'T WAIT TO GET HOME AND HAVE A BATH
BLOW THE HORN!
I CAN'T
CAN'T? WHY NOT?
BECAUSE THAT SPANIARD HAS JUST STABBED ME AND I AM DYING
BLOOD ALL OVER MY BEST SADDLE
OH, I KNOW. HORRIBLE STUFF ISN'T IT?

SO ROLAND DIED TO SAVE HIS KING. HE FOUGHT AGAINST FIVE HUGE ARMIES RATHER THAN SURRENDER.
SPLURCH
WHAT A KNIGHTLY NUTTER ... URRRGGGGH!
HE WHO FIGHTS AND RUNS AWAY...
...LIVES TO FIGHT ANOTHER DAY

ROLAND AND OLLY DIED LIKE HEROES. BUT CHARLEMAGNE WAS SAVED.

'The Song of Roland' is the oldest French tale around. It was written 500 years after the battle where Roland died, so it isn't all true. The story would have been sung by travelling poets – 'troubadours', the French called them. The knights would hear the poems and get the idea, 'That's how a good knight behaves!' There is a tombstone near the Roncevaux Pass showing the area where it is thought Roland died. One story says Roland was chopped down by a child. The killer kid, Iñigo Arista, went on to be first king of Navarre in Northern Spain. A boy who butchered big bold Roland? Believe it if you like.

A KNIGHT-TIME STORY

BULGARIA, AD 900

KNIGHTS WERE FEARSOME FIGHTERS ... YET THEY ENJOYED SOPPY STORIES AS WELL AS TROUBADOUR TALES OF TERROR. THEIR 'CHIVALRY' INCLUDED LOOKING AFTER LADIES ... ESPECIALLY LADIES IN TROUBLE. ONE OF THE MOST FAMOUS TALES FROM EUROPE WAS THE STORY OF HILDBURG AND HUGO. IT WAS SUPPOSED TO HAVE HAPPENED IN NORTHERN GREECE WHERE KING WALGUND RULED RUTHLESSLY...

ONCE UPON A TIME THERE WAS A BRAVE YOUNG KNIGHT CALLED PRINCE HUGO – THE SON OF THE EMPEROR ANZIUS OF BULGARIA.

WHERE WILL I FIND A WIFE GOOD ENOUGH FOR ME, PA?
YOU NEED A PRINCESS, HUGO. BEAUTIFUL AND RICH

RICH AND BEAUTIFUL PRINCESSES WERE RARE. EVERYBODY WANTED ONE AND THERE WEREN'T ENOUGH TO GO AROUND. BUT...

I HAVE HEARD THAT KING WALGUND OF THESSALONICA HAS A LOVELY DAUGHTER. BEAUTIFUL AND RICH. HER NAME IS HILDBURG

HILDBURG, EH? SOUNDS LIKE THE GAL FOR ME, PA. I'LL POP OFF AND MARRY HER THEN

NOT SO FAST, HUGO LAD. KING WALGUND LOVES HILDBURG SO MUCH HE HAS LOCKED HER IN A TOWER IN A FOREST FULL OF WILD WOLVES. NO MAN CAN GET NEAR HER
OH, FIDDLESTICKS. THAT'S A JOLLY ROTTEN THING TO DO TO ME. I WANT TO MARRY HER, PA. I SIMPLY HAVE TO
THEN YOU NEED A PLAN
OH, DRAT. I NEVER WAS ANY GOOD AT DRAWING
OF COURSE THE EMPEROR MEANT HE NEEDED A PLAN OF ACTION ... AND HE CAME UP WITH A WEIRD AND WILD PLOT THAT COULD NEVER WORK... OR COULD IT?
HUGO SPENT MONTHS LEARNING HOW TO EMBROIDER. THEN HE MADE HIMSELF SOME BEAUTIFUL DRESSES...
GOSH, MY FINGERS ARE SORE. THIS IS HARDER WORK THAN POUNDING A THOUSAND PEASANTS
THROB
GOD SPEED, MY SON ... AFTER YOU'VE HAD A SHAVE

AND OFF HE RODE, THROUGH THE WILD WOLVES, TO HILDBURG'S TOWER. HE HAD HIS STORY READY...
I AM A POOR LADY WHOSE BEASTLY BROTHER HAS THROWN HER OUT. TAKE PITY ON ME, PRINCESS
WOW! LOOK AT THAT DRESS! IF YOU CAN TEACH ME TO SEW LIKE THAT YOU ARE WELCOME
HILDBURG LOVED HER NEW PAL...
OOOOH! I DO LOVE YOUR DEEP VOICE, YOUR STRONG HANDS, YOUR BROAD SHOULDERS
YOU'RE NOT SO JOLLY BA
YOURSELF, PRINCESS
BUT HUGO HAD FORGOTTEN TO TAKE HIS RAZOR AND, AFTER A WEEK, HILDBURG STARTED TO SUSPECT HIM...
EXCUSE ME ... BUT I HAVE THE STRANGEST FEELING THAT YOU ARE REALLY A MAN DISGUISED AS A WOMAN
HOW ON EARTH DID YOU GUESS? HEIGH-HO
SUPPOSE YOUR OLD DAD WILL KILL ME THE

HILDBURG'S MAID WENT OFF TO FETCH A PRIEST AND THEY WERE MARRIED IN A TRICE ... OR I SHOULD SAY THEY WERE MARRIED IN A ROOM IN THE CASTLE. BUT HUGO KNEW THEY COULDN'T LIVE LIKE THAT FOREVER...

HUGO PUT ON HIS ARMOUR AND RODE OFF TO KING WALGUND'S PALACE. BUT WHEN HE GOT THERE HE WAS IN FOR A SURPRISE...
KING WALGUND? I AM HUGO OF BULGARIA, A KNIGHT AND...
EXCELLENT! I NEED ALL THE KNIGHTS I CAN GET TO JOIN ME IN A WAR AGAINST MY ENEMIES! WELCOME, SIR HUGO
HUGO FOUGHT SIDE-BY-SIDE WITH KING WALGUND. THEY WERE AWAY TWO YEARS AND THINGS HAD BEEN HAPPENING IN THE TALL TOWER. HILDBURG HAD A BABY BOY. ONE DAY HER MAID RUSHED IN WITH NEWS...
MY LADY, YOUR MOTHER THE QUEEN IS ON HER WAY TO VISIT YOU!
QUICK, TAKE THE BABY AND HIDE IT BY THE MOAT. MUMMY MUSTN'T SEE HIM
THE MAID DID AS SHE WAS TOLD. BUT WHEN THE QUEEN LEFT, AND THE MAID WENT TO FETCH THE BABY, THERE HE WAS ... OR SHOULD I SAY THERE HE WASN'T...
GONE!

THE BABY HAD CRAWLED OFF INTO THE FOREST WHERE IT WAS HAPPILY PLAYING WITH A PACK OF WOLF CUBS. BUT THE OLD WOLVES WERE ON THEIR WAY BACK TO THE LAIR ... OH DEAR...

LUCKILY HUGO AND KING WALGUND WERE ON THEIR WAY HOME TO THE PALACE WHEN WALGUND SAID...

LET'S TAKE A SHORT-CUT THROUGH THE FOREST OF WILD WOLVES

I'M JOLLY WELL NOT AFRAID

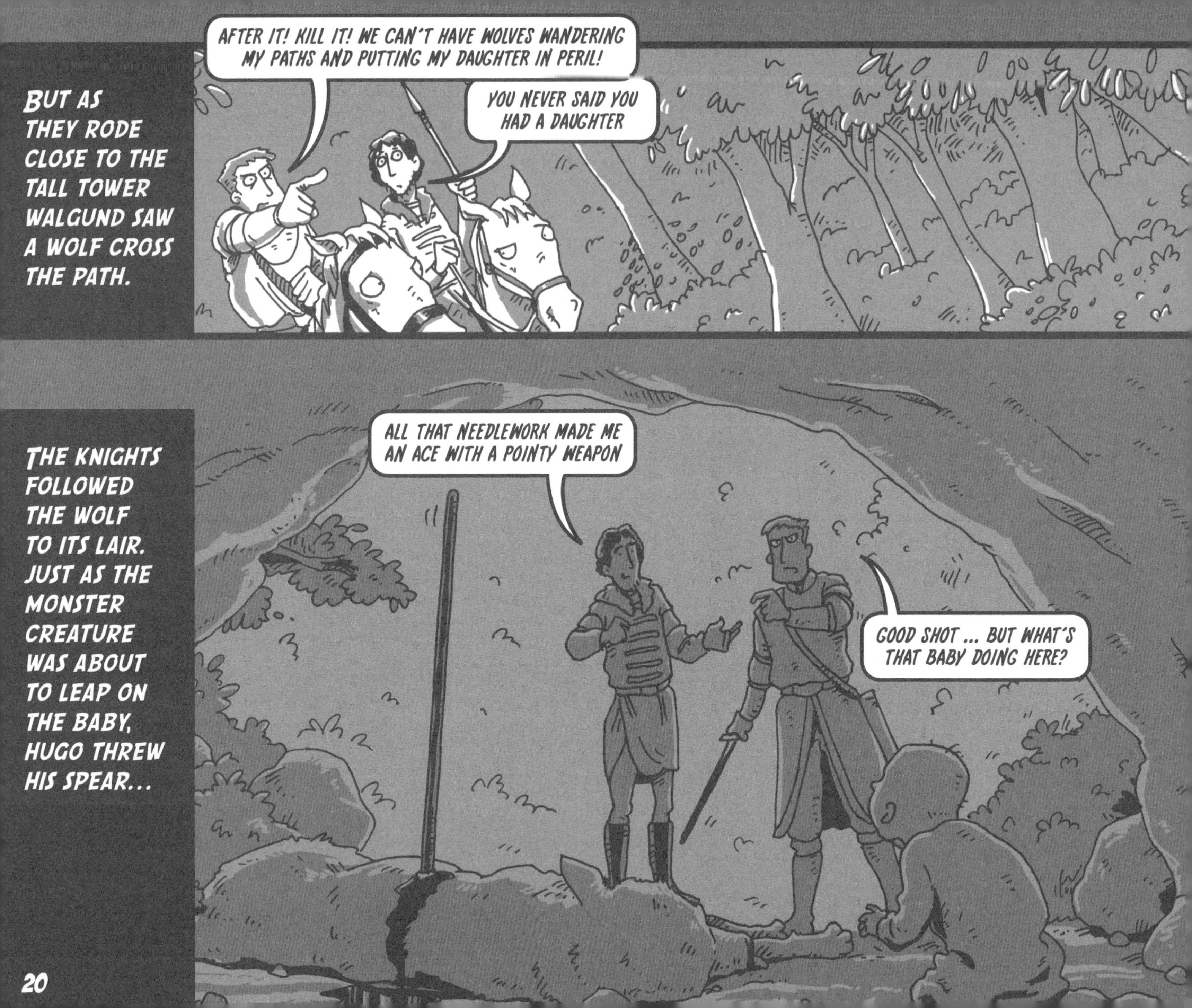
BUT AS THEY RODE CLOSE TO THE TALL TOWER WALGUND SAW A WOLF CROSS THE PATH.
AFTER IT! KILL IT! WE CAN'T HAVE WOLVES WANDERING MY PATHS AND PUTTING MY DAUGHTER IN PERIL!
YOU NEVER SAID YOU HAD A DAUGHTER
THE KNIGHTS FOLLOWED THE WOLF TO ITS LAIR. JUST AS THE MONSTER CREATURE WAS ABOUT TO LEAP ON THE BABY, HUGO THREW HIS SPEAR...
ALL THAT NEEDLEWORK MADE ME AN ACE WITH A POINTY WEAPON
GOOD SHOT ... BUT WHAT'S THAT BABY DOING HERE?

TELL YOU WHAT ... LET'S TAKE IT TO MY DAUGHTER'S TOWER. SHE'LL LOOK AFTER IT
JOLLY GOOD IDEA ... I'D LOVE TO MEET HER
WHEN THEY ARRIVED AT THE TOWER WITH THE LOST BABY, HILDBURG CLUTCHED THE BOY TO HER CHEST...
MY BABY ... MY DARLING SON
SON? MY GRANDSON? BUT WHO IS THE FATHER? NO MAN IS GOOD ENOUGH FOR YOU. WHO IS IT?
ACTUALLY, IT'S ME, YOUR MAJ

HUGO HAD FOUGHT BRAVELY IN WALGUND'S WARS. THE KING WAS REALLY RATHER PLEASED.
I'M REALLY RATHER PLEASED
BUT WHAT IS MY FINE SON'S NAME?
PHEW! THAT'S A RELIEF
I WAS WAITING FOR YOU TO RETURN HOME TO NAME HIM. THERE IS REALLY ONLY ONE NAME YOU CAN GIVE HIM NOW...
WOLF, OF COURSE!!!
AND THEY ALL LIVED HAPPILY EVER AFTER ... UNTIL THEY DIED

There is probably no truth in the story. But the important thing is the knights believed it and copied Hugo. They would do anything at all to win the woman they loved. They would fight, and even die, for their lady ... though only one knight, Ulrich of Lichtenstein, actually dressed as a woman to fight for his lady. He charged around Europe in a silk dress and hoped she would marry him if he defeated a hundred knights. But, in the end, his lady turned him down. Maybe she didn't fancy a man who wore a knight-dress?

GORY GEORGE

THE MIDDLE EAST, AD 300

HAVE YOU EVER MET A DRAGON? NO? COULD IT BE BECAUSE THE KNIGHTS OF OLD KILLED THEM ALL OFF? OF COURSE SOME HORRIBLE HISTORIANS SAY THERE NEVER WERE FIERY DRAGONS. THE 'KNIGHTS' WERE CHRISTIAN SAINTS AND THE 'DRAGONS' WERE JUST ENEMIES OF THE CHRISTIAN CHURCH. IS THAT THE TRUTH BEHIND THE LEGEND OF SAINT GEORGE AND THE DRAGON?

SOLDIERS LIKE GEORGE OF CAPPADOCIA – STRONG, HANDSOME AND A FANTASTIC FIGHTER

YEAH... WELL HE'S NOT THAT GOOD

HAVE THIS NOTICE PUT UP IN EVERY ROMAN CITY...

CITIZENS OF ROME
OUR WONDROUS EMPEROR DIOCLETIAN HEREBY RULES THAT IT IS AGAINST THE LAW TO BE A CHRISTIAN.
CHURCHES MUST BE DESTROYED AND BIBLES BURNED.
ANY REBEL WHO TRIES TO FIGHT FOR CHRISTIANS WILL BE EXECUTED. EXECUTED HORRIBLY! SO HORRIBLY YOU WOULDN'T WANT TO KNOW WHAT WE'LL DO TO THEM.
SO DON'T TRY IT. GOT THAT? GOOD.
SIGNED DIOCLETIAN

ROMAN SOLDIERS ARRESTED THE CHRISTIANS. SOME WERE BURNED ALIVE IN THEIR HOMES. OTHERS HAD STONES HUNG FROM THEIR NECKS, WERE TIED TOGETHER AND PUSHED INTO THE SEA. SOME HAD EYES PUT OUT, NOSES SLIT AND EARS CUT OFF.

GEORGE WAS IN THE CITY OF NICOMEDIA AND HE TORE DOWN THE EMPEROR'S NOTICE.
THE CHRISTIANS ARE GOOD AND HARMLESS
YOU'RE MAD! MAD! TAKE HIM AWAY AND TORTURE HIM TILL HE CHANGES HIS MIND
IT WILL BE A PLEASURE, BOSS
SEVEN YEARS LATER...
WELL? HAS GEORGE CHANGED HIS MIND?
NO, BOSS. WE'VE RIPPED OUT FINGERNAILS AND BURNED HIM WITH RED-HOT IRONS, WE'VE HUNG HIM UP BY THE FEET AND WE'VE BEATEN HIM TILL WE WERE EXHAUSTED
WE POISONED HI AND STARVED HI THEN WE TRIED TH NEW THING ... TI HIM TO THE RIM OF A WHEEL WIT SHARP SPIKES. SEVEN YEARS WASTED. NOTHIN WORKED

I SUPPOSE I'LL HAVE TO HAVE HIM EXECUTED. IT'S A SHAME BECAUSE HE'S STRONG, HANDSOME AND A FANTASTIC FIGHTER

SO GEORGE WAS BEHEADED.
RIGHT LADS LET'S CHOP HIM INTO PIECES, BURN THE BITS THEN BURY THEM
HARD WORK THAT

SOME LEGENDS SAY GEORGE WAS BEHEADED, CUT UP, BURNED AND BURIED **THREE** TIMES BEFORE HE FINALLY DIED. A BISHOP CALLED THEODOTUS DESCRIBED HIS HORRIBLE END...

And they pulverized him on a slab until his bones were crushed to pulp ... they struck his head with a hammer until his brains oozed through his nose ... then the emperor ordered them to saw him down the middle of his head and body.

SCRITCH

BUT WHAT IS CERTAIN IS HIS NAME BECAME A LEGEND AND STORIES GREW UP ABOUT HIM. AND IN THE STORIES, THE PAGAN EMPEROR BECAME A MONSTER...
THERE WAS ONCE A GREAT KNIGHT CALLED SAINT GEORGE. A MONSTER CAME TO THE LAND AND ATE ALL THE SHEEP AND COWS. THE PEOPLE WERE STARVING...
I BET. WHAT TIME'S DINNER, MUM?
THE MONSTER HAD A HUGE SCALY BODY, GREAT WINGS AND CRUEL CLAWS. WHEN IT BREATHED, IT BREATHED OUT FIRE...
THAT WOULD BE TO COOK THE SHEEP AND COWS BEFORE IT ATE THEM
THE MONSTER - THE 'DRAGON' IT WAS CALLED - STARTED EATING A CHILD EVERY MONTH. THE PARENTS HAD A LOTTERY TO SEE WHICH CHILD SHOULD DIE
AND THE WINNER IS...
A LOTTERY NOBODY WANTED TO WIN. HEH! HEH!
TREMBLE
X
V
IV

BUT ONE DAY THE KING'S DAUGHTER LOST THE LOTTERY. SHE WAS SENT TO THE DRAGON'S DEN AND CHAINED TO A ROCK TO WAIT FOR DEATH
FAIR ENOUGH
BUT ALONG CAME SAINT GEORGE... HE SET THE MAIDEN FREE AND TOOK THE BELT FROM AROUND HER DRESS
THAT WOULD BE TO BELT THE DRAGON WITH, I BET
WHEN GEORGE TIED THE BELT ROUND THE DRAGON'S NECK IT BECAME QUIET AND TAME. HE LED IT BACK TO THE CITY

GEORGE SAID HE WOULD KILL THE DRAGON IF THE PAGAN PEOPLE AGREED TO BECOME CHRISTIAN
AND DID THEY?

THE PEOPLE ALL AGREED TO BECOME CHRISTIAN ... SO GEORGE CHOPPED OFF THE DRAGON'S HEAD. THE END
AWWWW! POOR DRAGON

OF COURSE WHEN KNIGHTS WERE LOOKING FOR A SAINT, THEY CHOSE A WARRIOR AND A HERO ... GEORGE.

FORWARD, MEN ... FOR FREEDOM AND SAINT GEORGE!

GEORGE'S FLAG WAS A RED CROSS ON A WHITE FLAG. CHRISTIAN SOLDIERS WERE WEARING HIS CROSS IN 1098 WHEN GEORGE SHOWED UP AT THE BATTLE OF ANTIOCH AND HELPED THEM WIN. AND IF YOU BELIEVE THAT YOU PROBABLY BELIEVE IN THE TOOTH FAIRY.

BY GEORGE!

In the year 1348 King Edward III set up the 'Knights of the Garter' for the top knights in England. The badge of the Garter knights shows Saint George killing a dragon. And George became the special saint of England ... and Boy Scouts. So, if you ever have trouble with a dragon in your back garden you could try calling a Boy Scout.

RUTHLESS RULES

EUROPE, 1100s

KNIGHTS THOUGHT THEY WERE BETTER THAN COMMON SOLDIERS. THEY DIDN'T GO OUT TO KILL THEIR ENEMIES BUT TO CAPTURE THEM. THE BEATEN KNIGHTS HAD TO PAY TO GO FREE. IF A KNIGHT SURRENDERED TO YOU THEN YOU SPARED HIS LIFE. THAT WAS JUST ONE OF THE CURIOUS RULES OF CHIVALRY A KNIGHT WOULD FOLLOW. A STUDENT KNIGHT - A SQUIRE - WOULD HAVE TO LEARN LOTS OF OTHERS...

OF COURSE YOU DON'T LET ANYONE PUSH YOU OR YOUR FAMILY AROUND...
IF YOU ARE INSULTED, SEEK REVENGE
SEEK REVENGE IF YOUR SISTER IS INSULTED
YEAH. THAT'S MORE LIKE IT
BUT I HAVEN'T GOT A SISTER
NOW YOU MAY WONDER WHY WE BOTHER TO FIGHT. ANYONE KNOW?
PLEASE, SIR, A KNIGHT FIGHTS FOR A LADY
CORRECT. WELL DONE, YOUNG MAN. HERE'S WHAT YOU DO FOR YOUR LADY...
FIGHT FOR HER
WRITE BEAUTIFUL POETRY FOR HER
DO BRAVE DEEDS FOR HER
DIE FOR HER
POETRY?
ROSES ARE RED, VIOLETS ARE BLUE, AND YOUR BEAUTIFUL FACE CAN BE SEEN IN A ZOO

A YOUNG KNIGHT SHOULD ONLY WOO A NOBLE WOMAN. REMEMBER, NO PEASANTS. GO WOO A QUEEN IF YOU CAN. A KNIGHT SHOULD KNOCK AT HER DOOR UNTIL IT OPENS. NEVER GIVE UP
NO!
YES!
BUT WHAT DO I DO WHEN SHE OPENS IT?
GIVE HER A
CUDDLE OF COU
CUDDLING IS ALLOWED BUT DO IT IN SECRET. PUBLIC CUDDLING IS A BAD IDEA. IF THE WOMAN ISN'T MARRIED THEN HER DAD WILL GET UPSET WITH YOU. IF THE WOMAN IS MARRIED THEN HER HUSBAND WILL GET UPSET WITH YOU
DAD
HUSBAND
OOOOH! I'M NOT SURE IF SHE'S WORTH THE BOTHER

MARRIED WOMEN ARE BEST. THEY PROBABLY MARRIED SOME LORD AS PART OF A DEAL ABOUT HER LAND. SHE WILL BE BORED AND LONELY
SORRY, ROBERT, BUT SHE'D HAVE TO BE VERY BORED AND VERY LONELY TO FANCY YOU
THANKS, MATE
BEFORE YOU CAN GO INTO BATTLE, A KNIGHT HAS TO PRACTISE. SOMETIMES KNIGHTS HAVE PRACTICE BATTLES CALLED 'MÊLÉES'. A SORT OF FREE-FOR-ALL
OOOOH! I HOPE I DON'T GET HURT
NAH! THIS SHOULD BE FUN
RIGHT, LADS, I WANT YOU TO SPLIT INTO TWO TEAMS OF ABOUT A HUNDRED A SIDE. THE PLAYING FIELD IS TEN SQUARE MILES OF LORD CRINGLE'S FIELDS, RIVERS AND WOODS

TWO RULES. FIRST, THIS FIELD IS THE 'SAFE AREA' - YOU CAN'T TOUCH A KNIGHT WHEN HE IS IN HERE
SECOND RULE - DON'T TRY TO KILL ANYONE. EVEN IN A REAL BATTLE YOU TRY TO CAPTURE THE ENEMY. OF COURSE A FEW OF YOU MAY DIE ... BUT IT'S ALL PART OF THE FUN
I FEEL POORLY. I WISH I HAD A NOTE FROM ME MUM TO GET OUT OF THIS GAME
MOST KIDS WRITE THEIR OWN
ON YOUR MARKS ... GO!
PLEASE SIR ... HE'S HITTING ME BEFORE I'VE EVEN GOT MY HELMET ON...
BOCK!
THAT'S ALLOWE
... TAKE THAT!

I MAY SPEND A LOT OF TIME HERE
DOOF!
AW, SIRRRR! THERE'S FIVE OF THEM ALL ATTACKING ME. IT'S NOT FAIR
YES IT IS

PLEASE SIR, THAT KNIGHT USED A BOW AND ARROW. HE CAN'T DO THAT!
OH YES HE CAN
HE JUMPED OUT FROM BEHIND A TREE. IS HE ALLOWED?
IF IT'S A BACON TREE ... IT'S A HAM-BUSH. AMBUSH GEDDIT? HEH! HEH!
ME HORSE RAN OFF. THEY CAN'T ATTACK ME WHEN I'M ON FOOT
WANT TO BET?

NOW THEY'VE STABBED ME IN HE BACK. YOU CAN'T LET THEM DO SNEAKY THINGS LIKE THAT
IT'S ALL PART OF A MÊLÉE
OOOOF! HE HIT ME BELOW THE BELT
YEP. THAT'S FAIR ENOUGH. THIS ISN'T FUN FIGHTING
WHUMP!
I'M WAVING A WHITE FLAG ... SURRENDER
NO WHITE FLAGS ALLOWED

AND WHAT HAVE YOU LEARNED IN KNIGHT SCHOOL TODAY?
SOME KNIGHTS GET CARRIED AWAY

Mêlées were very, very rough and all sorts of tricks were allowed. One idea was to join the mêlée half an hour after the start. The fighters were worn out – you could just go in and grab a few exhausted knights. Some grabbed a wounded knight AFTER the mêlée had finished and the knights were on their way back to dinner. No wonder knights died in these 'practice' fights.

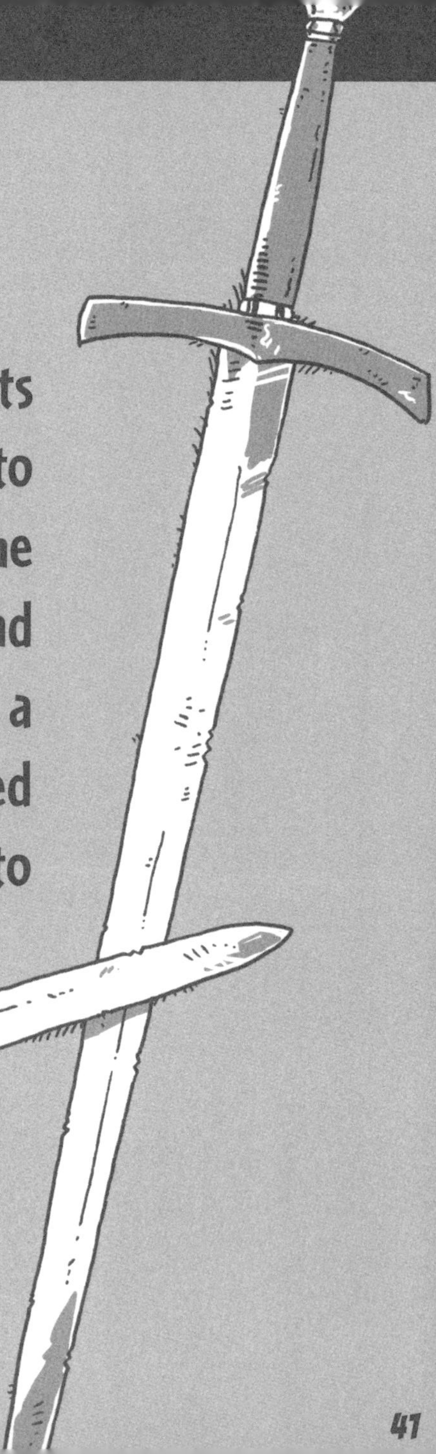

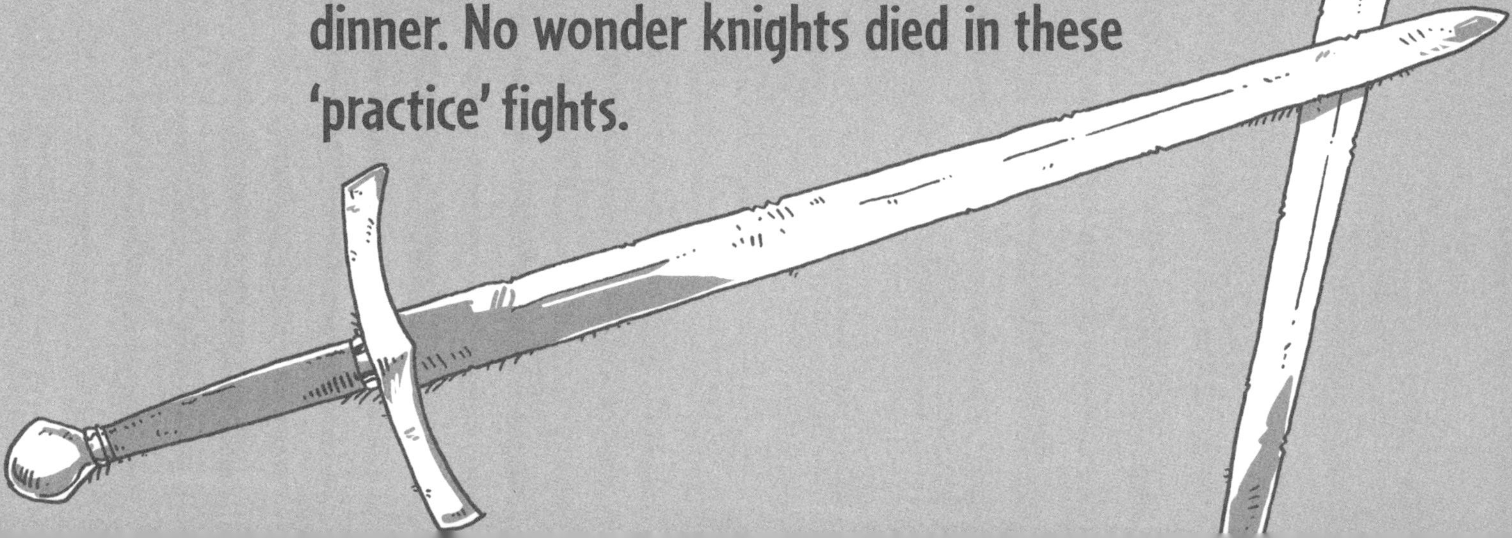

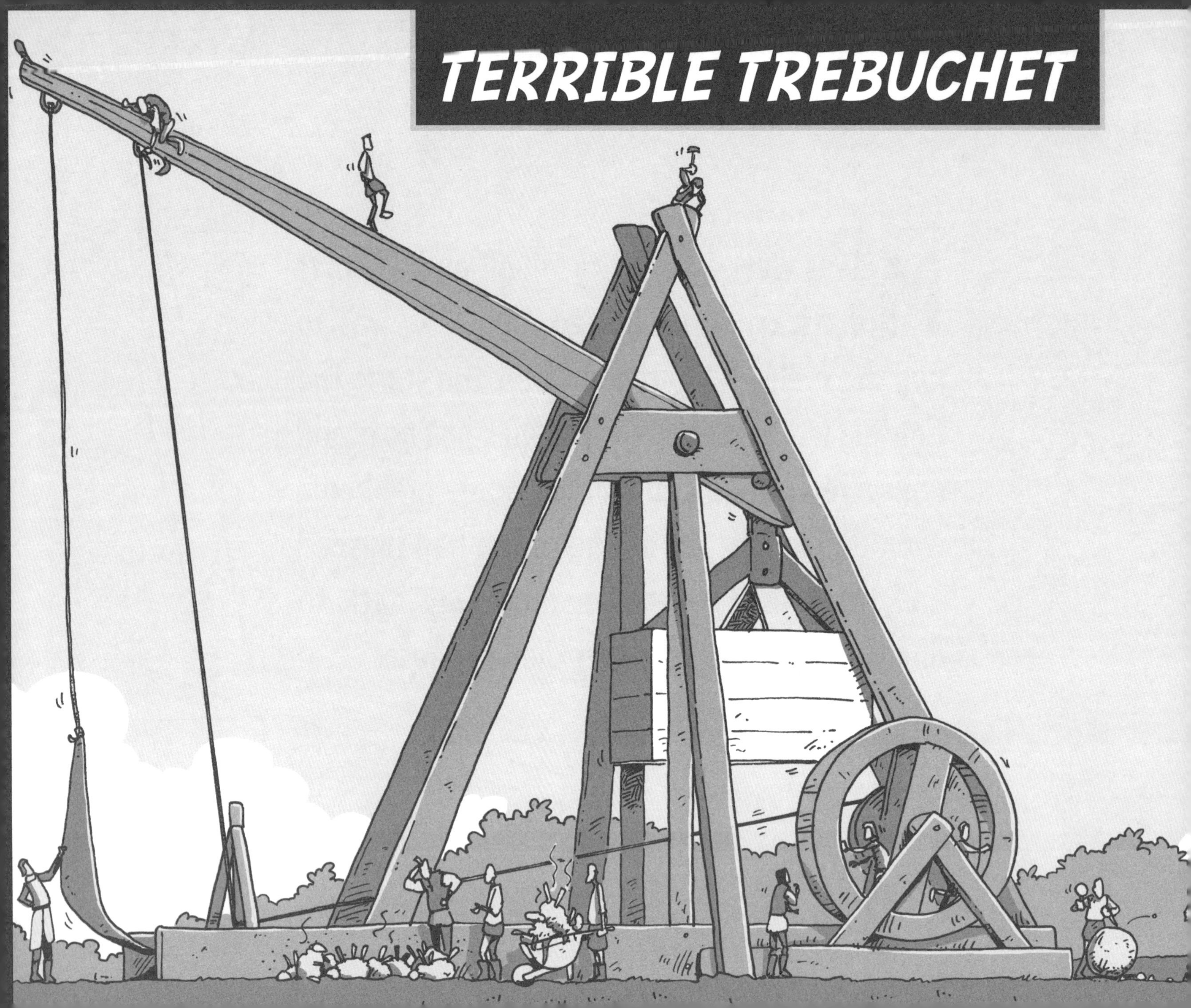
TERRIBLE TREBUCHET

Fig.1
Fig.2
Fig.3

CRUEL CRUSADES

PALESTINE, AD 1097

KNIGHTS KILLED OTHER KNIGHTS. THEN THE HEAD OF THE CHRISTIAN CHURCH - THE POPE - SAID, 'THAT IS WICKED. YOU WILL GO TO HELL. IF YOU **HAVE** TO KILL SOMEBODY THEN KILL PEOPLE WHO AREN'T CHRISTIANS. THAT WAY YOU WILL GO TO HEAVEN WHEN YOU DIE. GO OFF AND KILL THE MUSLIMS WHO ARE LIVING IN OUR HOLY LAND.' AND THE KNIGHTS OF EUROPE WERE HAPPY TO DO THAT. THEY SET OFF ON 'CRUSADES'.

IN 1095 POPE URBAN II DECIDED IT WAS TIME THE CHRISTIANS TOOK OVER JERUSALEM FOR THE CHRISTIAN CHURCH.
WE DON'T HAVE AN EXCUSE TO INVADE THE HOLY LAND, POPE URBAN
GATHER THE BEST KNIGHTS TOGETHER AND I'LL THINK OF SOMETHING
URBAN TRIED THE USUAL WAR-MAKER'S TRICK OF TELLING HIS PEOPLE HOW CRUEL THE ENEMY COULD BE.
THE TURKS CUT OPEN THE BELLIES OF CHRISTIANS THAT THEY WANT TO TORMENT WITH A LOATHSOME DEATH. THEY TEAR OUT THEIR ORGANS AND TIE THEM TO A STAKE. THEY DRAG THEIR VICTIMS ROUND THE STAKE AND FLOG THEM. THEY KILL THEM AS THEY LIE FLAT ON THE GROUND WITH THEIR GUTS OUT
I FEEL ANGRY
I FEEL SICK

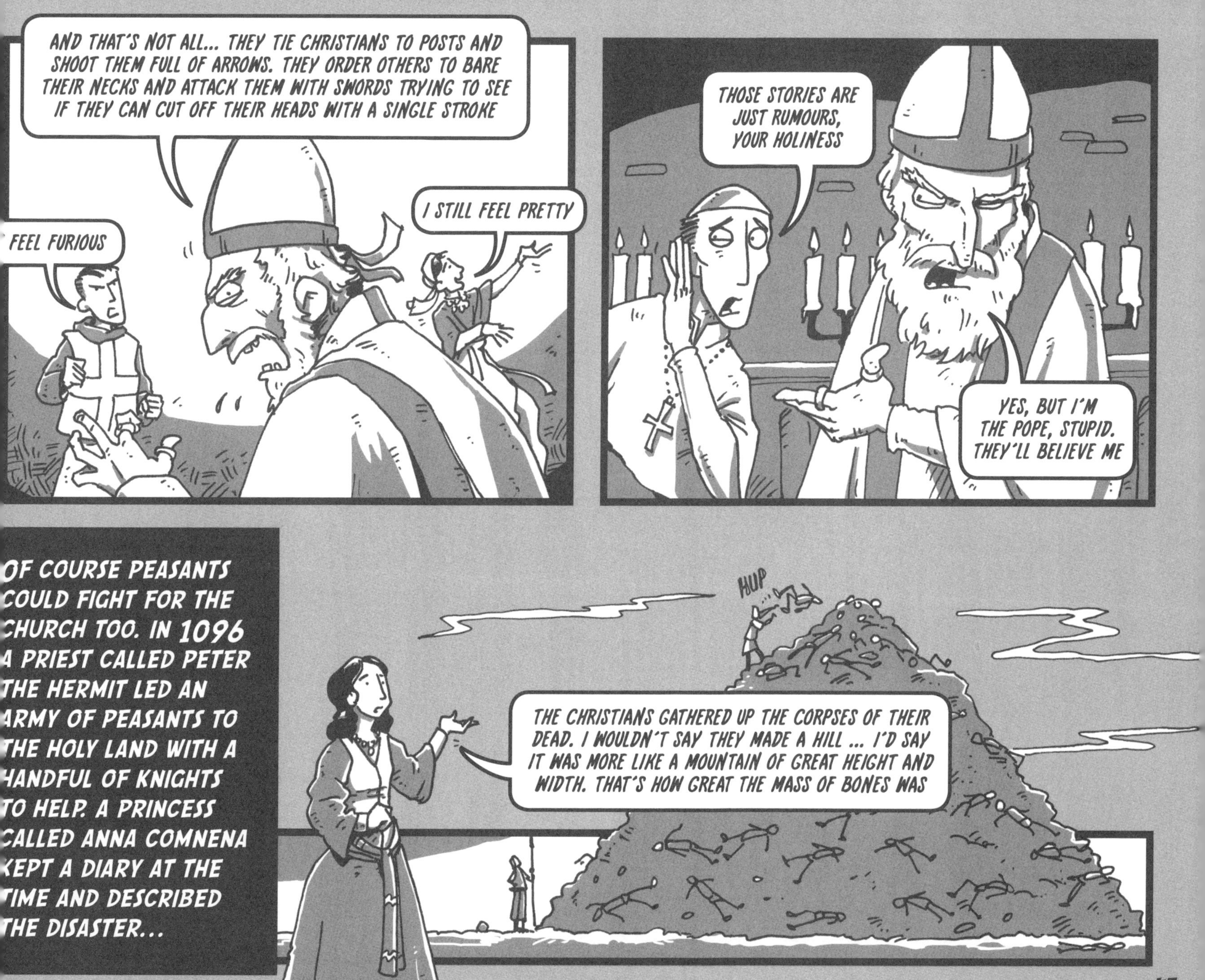
AND THAT'S NOT ALL... THEY TIE CHRISTIANS TO POSTS AND SHOOT THEM FULL OF ARROWS. THEY ORDER OTHERS TO BARE THEIR NECKS AND ATTACK THEM WITH SWORDS TRYING TO SEE IF THEY CAN CUT OFF THEIR HEADS WITH A SINGLE STROKE
FEEL FURIOUS
I STILL FEEL PRETTY
THOSE STORIES ARE JUST RUMOURS, YOUR HOLINESS
YES, BUT I'M THE POPE, STUPID. THEY'LL BELIEVE ME
OF COURSE PEASANTS COULD FIGHT FOR THE CHURCH TOO. IN 1096 A PRIEST CALLED PETER THE HERMIT LED AN ARMY OF PEASANTS TO THE HOLY LAND WITH A HANDFUL OF KNIGHTS TO HELP. A PRINCESS CALLED ANNA COMNENA KEPT A DIARY AT THE TIME AND DESCRIBED THE DISASTER...
HUP
THE CHRISTIANS GATHERED UP THE CORPSES OF THEIR DEAD. I WOULDN'T SAY THEY MADE A HILL ... I'D SAY IT WAS MORE LIKE A MOUNTAIN OF GREAT HEIGHT AND WIDTH. THAT'S HOW GREAT THE MASS OF BONES WAS

OF COURSE AN ARMY OF KNIGHTS WOULD DO MUCH BETTER ... OR WOULD THEY? THEY SET OFF ON SHIPS AND OVER LAND AND ARRIVED AT ANTIOCH BY 1097...

CONSTANTINOPLE

ROME

ANTIOCH

THEY DIDN'T HAVE ENOUGH MEN TO ATTACK THE LARGE CITY SO THE TOP KNIGHT, BOHEMOND, NEEDED A SNEAKY PLAN.

I NEED A SNEAKY PLAN
WHY NOT PAY ONE OF THE GUARDS TO LEAVE A GATE OPEN?
HAH! HE WANTS A SNEAKY PLAN, NOT A STUPID PLAN
I'VE DECIDED ... TO PAY ONE OF THE GUARDS TO LEAVE A GATE OPEN
GREAT IDEA, MY LORD!

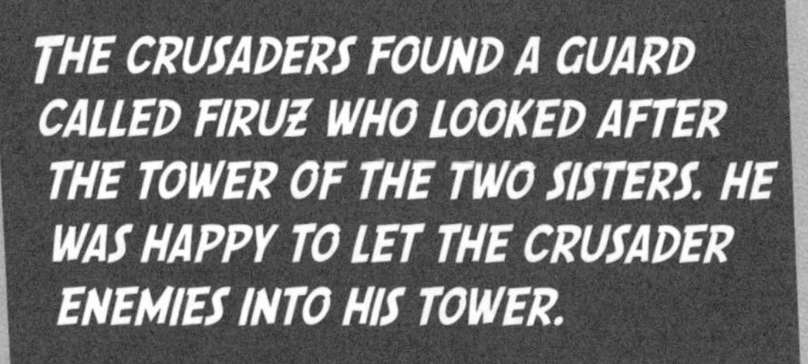

THE CRUSADERS FOUND A GUARD CALLED FIRUZ WHO LOOKED AFTER THE TOWER OF THE TWO SISTERS. HE WAS HAPPY TO LET THE CRUSADER ENEMIES INTO HIS TOWER.

'LL LET YOU IN. YOUR SIEGE IS STARVING ME TO DEATH. I TRIED TO HIDE SOME GRAIN BUT MY COMMANDER FOUND IT AND HE FINED ME. I HATE HIM
WE'LL FEED YOU WELL

I ALSO CAUGHT MY COMMANDER CUDDLING MY WIFE. I DON'T WANT MUCH. JUST MY REVENGE. IF I LET YOU AND YOUR MEN IN THROUGH MY TOWER WILL YOU PROMISE TO KILL HIM?

IT WILL BE A PLEASURE

TWENTY THOUSAND CRUSADERS SLIPPED INTO THE CITY.

KILL THEM ALL!

ALL THE MEN, YOU MEAN? NOT THE WOMEN AND KIDS?

HE SAID **ALL**. IT'S A NICE CHOPPING TRIP FOR US

BUT BOHEMOND FORGOT SOMETHING...
EXCUSE ME SIR, BUT THERE'S NO FOOD IN THE CITY. THE PEOPLE ATE IT ALL
GO OUT AND GET SOME
WE CAN'T. AN ENEMY ARMY HAS ARRIVED. WE ARE THE ONES TRAPPED AND STARVING IN THE CITY NOW
OH, SNOTBALLS
THERE WAS ONLY ONE THING TO DO...
WHAT CAN WE DO?
RIDE OUT AND ATTACK THEM

A MAD MONK CALLED PETER BARTHOLOMEW SAID HE FOUND A HOLY SPEAR INSIDE THE CITY. IT WAS A MIRACLE, A GOOD LUCK CHARM FOR THE CRUSADERS.

ATTACK THE PAGANS! SPEAR TODAY, GONE TOMORROW

THE CRUSADERS RODE OUT WITH ONLY A HUNDRED FIT HORSES. THEY WOULD BE MASSACRED. THEN ANOTHER 'MIRACLE' OCCURRED...

OK! IN THE HILLS! AN ARMY OF MEN ON WHITE HORSES WITH WHITE BANNERS
IT'S SAINT GEORGE HIMSELF COMING TO RESCUE US. A GOLDEN OLDIE
HE'S BEEN DEAD 700 YEARS. HE'LL BE A GOLDEN MOULDY

THE CRUSADERS WON THE BATTLE. BUT WHO WERE THE MYSTERIOUS ARMY?

IT'S AN ARMY OF FRIENDS FROM TURKEY - NOT ST GEORGE AND NOT A MIRACLE
IT'S A MIRACLE THAT OUR FRIENDS ARRIVED AT JUST THE RIGHT TIME

IF SAINT GEORGE WAS HELPING, THEN WHY WASN'T HE AROUND WHEN THE PLAGUE STRUCK THE CRUSADERS IN ANTIOCH?
LET'S GET OUT OF THIS PLACE. LET'S HEAD FOR JERUSALEM
POKE
AGAIN THEY CAPTURED A CITY WITH NO FOOD. AGAIN THEY MASSACRED THE PEOPLE. A WRITER SAID...
The crusaders, excited by such a great victory, rushed through the streets and into the houses and mosques killing all that they met, men, women and children alike.
All that afternoon and all through the night the massacre went on. When Raymond of Aguilers went to visit the temple the next morning he had to pick his way through corpses and blood that reached up to his knees.
BUT THIS TIME THEY DIDN'T WASTE THE CORPSES. A KNIGHT WROTE...
OUR TROOPS BOILED PAGAN ADULTS IN COOKING POTS, AND ROASTED CHILDREN ON SPITS AND ATE THEM GRILLED

THE CRUSADERS WROTE TO THE POPE TO SAY 'SORRY' FOR EATING PEOPLE.
I FORGIVE THEM. GOD SAYS IT IS ALL RIGHT TO EAT A PAGAN IF YOU ARE STARVING. WHICH REMINDS ME ... WHAT'S FOR DINNER?
A CRUSADER HAPPY MEAL ... PAGAN PUDDING WITH PEAS AND PARSNIPS

That victory at Jerusalem didn't do the Crusaders much good. The Turks fought back and defeated the First Crusade in the end. A Second Crusade set out to rescue the first lot. They failed. Then a Third Crusade, with England's King Richard the Lionheart, tried again. Richard was up against tough Turk Saladin and failed. Lots of Turks and Christians died horrible deaths but their deaths did not change anything. By 1291, not quite 200 years after the First Crusade, the Christians lost their last city in the Holy Land.

KNIGHTS KNIGHT-MARE

PALESTINE, AD 1119

YOU MAY THINK MONKS ARE MEN OF PEACE. BUT THERE WAS ONE BAND OF WARRIOR MONKS WHO WERE AS SAVAGE AS ANY SOLDIERS IN HISTORY. THERE IS AN OLD SAYING THAT 'IF YOU LIVE BY THE SWORD YOU DIE BY THE SWORD.' IT WAS TRUE FOR THE TEMPLARS. THEY LIVED BY TERROR AND THEY DIED BY TERROR. THEIR TALE IS A REAL KNIGHT-MARE...

THE FIRST CRUSADE CAPTURED JERUSALEM AND CHRISTIANS STARTED VISITING THE CITY. THE CITY WAS SAFE, BUT THE JOURNEY WASN'T...
BANDITS!
SO TWO FRENCH KNIGHTS, HUGUES DE PAYENS, AND HIS RELATIVE GODFREY DE SAINT-OMER, CAME UP WITH A PLAN...
WE NEED A BAND OF KNIGHTS TO GUARD THE CHRISTIAN PILGRIMS
BUT THE GUARDS HAVE TO BE HOLY MEN

AT FIRST THERE WERE JUST NINE TEMPLAR KNIGHTS GUARDING THE CHRISTIAN PILGRIMS. THEY WERE SO POOR THEY CAME UP WITH A SPECIAL BANNER...

THE IDEA WAS SO POPULAR THE PEOPLE OF EUROPE GAVE THE TEMPLARS LOTS OF MONEY, TREASURES AND LAND. THE POPE WAS A BIG FAN OF THE MONK-IN-A-CAN IDEA.

TEMPLARS CAN TRAVEL WHEREVER THEY WANT, PAY NO TAXES AND DON'T HAVE TO OBEY ANY RULERS ... EXCEPT ME, OF COURSE
NICE ONE, YOUR POPESHIP

50 YEARS AFTER THEY STARTED, THE TEMPLARS HAD BECOME A LARGE ARMY. THEY WERE THE TOUGHEST OF KNIGHTS AND ALWAYS AT THE FRONT OF THE BATTLES - A SPOT KNOWN AS THE 'VANGUARD' (OR THE VAN).

I'M THE MAN IN A CAN IN THE VAN

AT THE 1177 BATTLE OF MONTGISARD A BAND OF 500 TEMPLAR KNIGHTS LED THE WAY IN BEATING AN ENEMY OF MORE THAN 26,000 SOLDIERS. THE ENEMY LEADER, SALADIN, JUST ESCAPED ON A RACING CAMEL.

MAN IN A CAN IN THE VAN? TIME WE RAN!

TEMPLARS WERE AN ODD SORT OF KNIGHT-CLUB WITH STRANGE RULES.
RULE 1 ... YOU MUST ALWAYS LEAVE OUR TEMPLE BY THE FRONT DOOR
THAT'S TO STOP ANYONE SNEAKING OUT TO ENJOY THEMSELVES
WE DON'T HUNT ANIMALS FOR SPORT THE WAY OTHER KNIGHTS DO... YOU MAY ONLY HUNT FOR LIONS
IS THAT TRUE?
HE'S NOT LION
TEMPLARS WILL NOT GAMBLE, DRINK TOO MUCH OR GO OUT WITH WOMEN
NO BETS, NO BOOZE, NO BABES

AND THE PUNISHMENTS ARE FEARSOME... YOU CAN BE LOCKED IN A DUNGEON FOR LIFE IF YOU BREAK A TEMPLAR RULE

IT'S THE CLINK IF YOU DRINK

THE TEMPLARS GREW SO RICH THEY STARTED LENDING MONEY ... THEY SET UP BANKS.

WE'RE STINKING RICH
YES I'M A STUNK MONK

AND, OF COURSE, IN TIME PEOPLE BECAME JEALOUS OF THE TEMPLAR RICHES. PEOPLE LIKE KING PHILIP IV OF FRANCE.

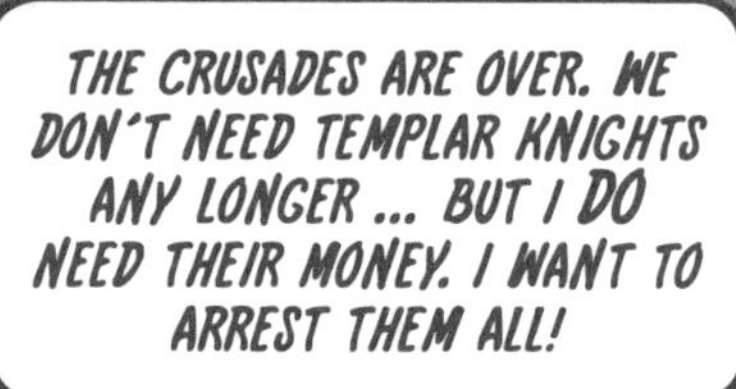

THE CRUSADES ARE OVER. WE DON'T NEED TEMPLAR KNIGHTS ANY LONGER ... BUT I DO NEED THEIR MONEY. I WANT TO ARREST THEM ALL!

POPE CLEMENT SAID...

GO AHEAD, KING PHIL ... JU
MAKE SURE I GET MY SHAR

ON FRIDAY 13 OCTOBER 1307, PHILIP'S OFFICERS ARRESTED EVERY TEMPLAR KNIGHT IN THE LAND.
JACQUES DE MOLAY, GRAND MASTER OF THE TEMPLE, YOU ARE UNDER ARREST!
ON WHAT CHARGE?
THERE ARE 127 CHARGES, INCLUDING SPITTING AND PEEING ON THE HOLY CROSS...
NEVER!
WORSHIPPING A MYSTERIOUS HEAD ... AND DEVIL WORSHIP! HOW DO YOU PLEAD?
NOT GUILTY!

TORTURE HIM AND THE REST OF HIS EVIL KNIGHTS
NOW HOW DO YOU PLEAD?
OUCH! GUILTY!
HE MUST GO TO PRISON FOR LIFE - AND THE TEMPLAR WEALTH MUST BE GIVEN UP ... TO ME!
BUT, IN PRISON, DE MOLAY DID A BRAVE THING. HE CHANGED HIS STORY.
THE TEMPLARS AND I ARE NOT GUILTY!
CHANGING A CONFESSION? THERE IS ONLY ONE PUNISHMENT FOR THAT. BURN HIM!

DE MOLAY, AND MANY OTHER TEMPLARS, WERE TAKEN TO THE STAKE ON 18 MARCH 1314. THEY WERE CONDEMNED TO DIE IN AGONY OVER A SLOW FIRE. AS HE DIED, DE MOLAY CRIED A CURSE...
I SHALL MEET YOU AND POPE CLEMENT BY GOD'S SEAT BEFORE A YEAR IS PAST. YOU AND YOUR FAMILY, FOR THIRTEEN GENERATIONS, WILL BE CURSED!

Curses are nonsense, aren't they? A month after the execution of the Templars Pope Clement died. Seven months later the torturing King Philip followed him to the grave – just as De Molay said he would. Philip died during a hunt when he was ripped apart by a wild boar.

Spooky, eh?

The bravest knights in history WEREN'T beaten by their enemies ... they were beaten by the people who were supposed to be their friends.

A HARD DAY'S KNIGHT

CRÉCY, NORTHERN FRANCE
26 AUGUST 1346

BY THE 1340S THE CRUSADES WERE LOST. THE KNIGHTS OF EUROPE HAD NO PAGANS TO FIGHT. BUT THE KING OF ENGLAND, EDWARD III, STARTED TO CLAIM HE SHOULD BE KING OF FRANCE. OF COURSE THE FRENCH GOT A BIT UPSET. IT MEANT WAR. THE FRENCH KNIGHTS AGAINST THE ENGLISH. THE WAR WENT ON 116 YEARS AND IS KNOWN AS THE HUNDRED YEARS WAR. AND THE KNIGHTS STRUGGLED AGAINST A STRANGE NEW ENEMY ... THE PEASANT WITH A BOW AND ARROW. SOME PEOPLE SAY IT WAS THE END OF THE DAYS OF KNIGHTS ... THE END OF CHIVALRY.

EDWARD HAD JUST 4,000 KNIGHTS IN ARMOUR. HE ALSO HAD ABOUT 12,000 FOOT SOLDIERS. THEY WERE MOSTLY ARMED WITH BOWS, ARROWS AND NASTY LITTLE KNIVES.

OF COURSE KING EDWARD WILL PAY YOU...
WHY DIDN'T YOU SAY? PACK MY BAGS
MINE TOO
BYE, LOVE. WE'LL KEEP A WELCOME IN THE HILLSIDES, TILL YOU COME HOME AGAIN TO WALES
SO LONG AS THEY COME HOME WITH LOTS OF LOVELY CASH, BRONWYN

KING PHILIP VI OF FRANCE WAS WAITING FOR THEM. BUT HE HAD TWICE AS MANY KNIGHTS AND FOOT SOLDIERS.
OH DEAR, OH DEAR. I'VE NEVER SEEN SO MANY PEOPLE
SO MANY PEOPLE ALL WANTING TO KILL US...

EDWARD MADE CAMP AT THE TOP OF A HILL NEAR CRÉCY VILLAGE. HE LOOKED OUT FROM THE TOP OF A WINDMILL.

BUT THE FRENCH COULDN'T WAIT TO ATTACK. THE KNIGHTS WERE DESPERATE TO FIGHT BEFORE NIGHT. KING PHILIP COULDN'T STOP THEM...

THE FRENCH CROSSBOW SOLDIERS WEREN'T READY...
OUR SHIELDS ARE STILL IN THE SUPPLY WAGONS
STOP WHINGEING. YOU WON'T NEED THEM
BUT JUST BEFORE THE FRENCH ATTACKED THERE WAS A SHOWER OF RAIN.
NO SHIELDS FOR SHELTER. OUR BOW STRINGS ARE SOAKED! THE SHOTS WON'T HAVE ANY POWER...
JUST GET ON WITH IT AND DO AS YOU ARE TOLD

THE ENGLISH AND WELSH BOWMEN HAD ROLLED UP THEIR BOW STRINGS TILL THE STORM PASSED.
RIGHT, LADS, HERE THEY COME ... READY?
READY

THE ENGLISH ARCHERS FIRED TWELVE SHOTS A MINUTE ... THE FRENCH CROSSBOWS COULD ONLY MANAGE TWO. THE FRENCH FELL LIKE TURKEYS AT CHRISTMAS...

RUN FOR YOUR LIFE!

AS THE CROSSBOW SOLDIERS RAN BACKWARDS, THE FRENCH KNIGHTS RODE FORWARD ... STRAIGHT OVER THEIR OWN CROSSBOW SOLDIERS.

SERVES YOU RIGHT, YOU COWARDS
CRUNCH!

THE FRENCH HAD TO CROSS A SWAMP AND A STREAM. ARROWS FROM THE ENGLISH AND WELSH LONGBOWS PUNCHED HOLES IN THEIR ARMOUR AND BIGGER HOLES IN THEIR HORSES...

IF I COULD GET TO THE ENGLISH I'D KILL THEM

FEW FRENCH
IGHTS GOT
ROUGH AND
EN REACHED
WARD'S SON,
E BLACK
INCE...
CLANG
I ASKED MY DAD TO SEND HELP BUT HE JUST TOLD ME TO LOOK AFTER MYSELF. THANKS, DAD
E FRENCH
ERE
IVEN BACK
D KING
ILIP TOLD
EM TO
TREAT...
LOOKS LIKE WE WON
BUT WE'RE NOT FINISHED YET, BOYO. TIME TO USE OUR LITTLE KNIVES
E
CHERS
N DOWN
THE
UNDED
ENCH
IGHTS...
I SURRENDER... MY FAMILY WILL PAY A RANSOM
SORRY ... I'M A WELSH PEASANT. WE DO THINGS DIFFERENTLY IN WALES

THEY PUSHED THE KNIVES INTO THE JOINTS IN THE ARMOUR.
WHAT ABOUT CHIVALRY? IS THIS THE END OF CHIVALRY?
CHIVALRY? I CAN'T EVEN SPELL IT
LET'S FACE IT DAFYDD, YOU CAN'T EVEN SPELL YOUR OWN NAME, NEVER MIND SPELL 'CHIVALRY'
PEASANTS KILLING KNIGHTS, EH? SEEMS ODD
WAR WILL NEVER BE THE SAME AGAIN
THE WELSH ARCHERS RETURNED HOME. THEY WERE GIVEN AN ACRE OF LAND AND MADE FREE MEN.
I'M A FREE MAN, MY LOVELY!
NOT WHILE YOU'RE MARRIED TO ME, BOYO. NOW GET OUT THERE AND START PLOUGHING OUR ACRE
YOU TELL HIM. THEY CAN BOSS A FRENCH KNIGHT BUT THEY CAN'T BOSS A WELSH WOMAN

The Battle of Crécy was just the start of the terrible, long war. Kings came and went. The knights tried to beat the power of the longbow but another weapon came along to defeat them ... the gun. Cannon blew apart even the toughest armour.

After 90 years of war the French were battered. The French Queen even agreed that England's King Henry V could have his French throne when her husband, mad King Charles, died. It looked like the end for France. But they reckoned without a peasant ... and this one was a girl.

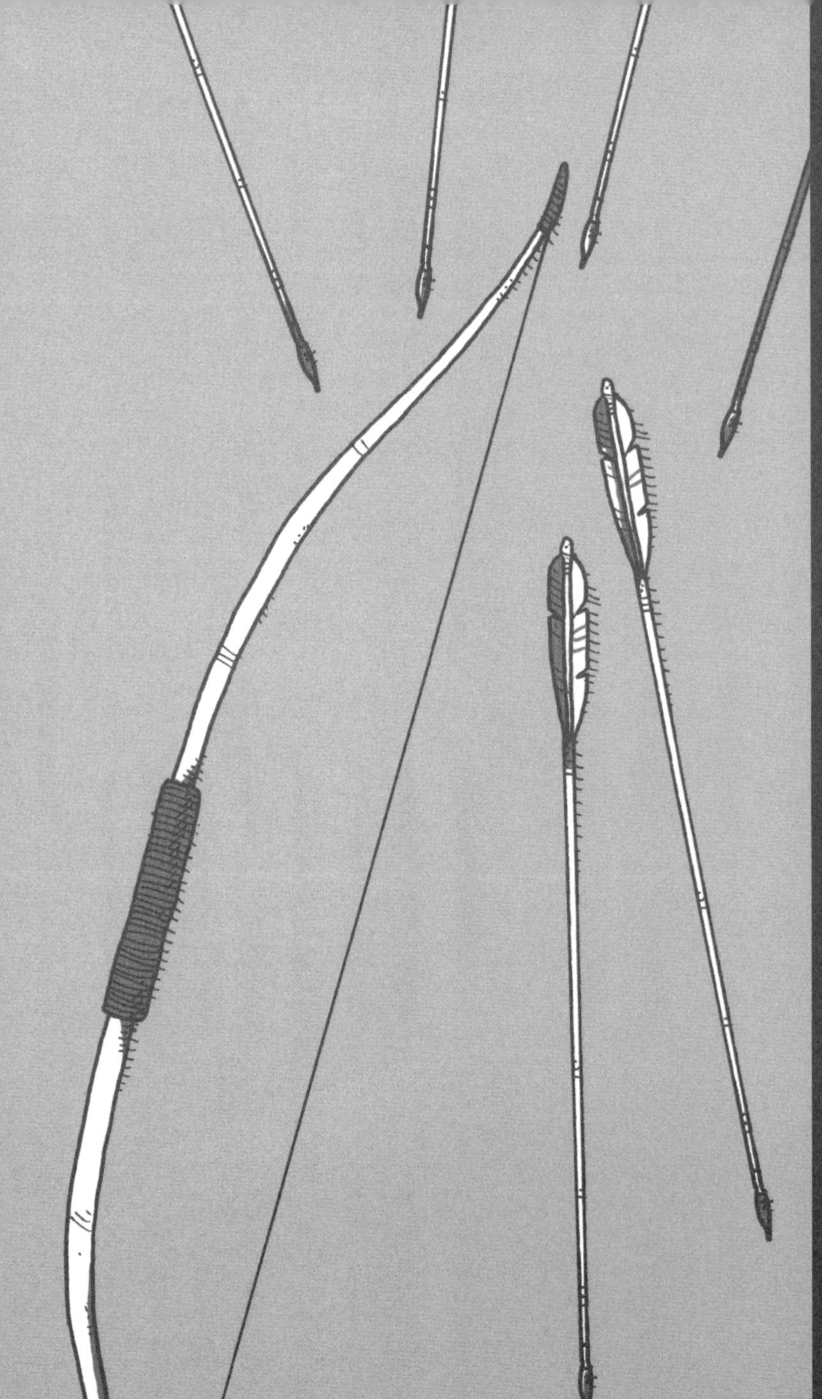

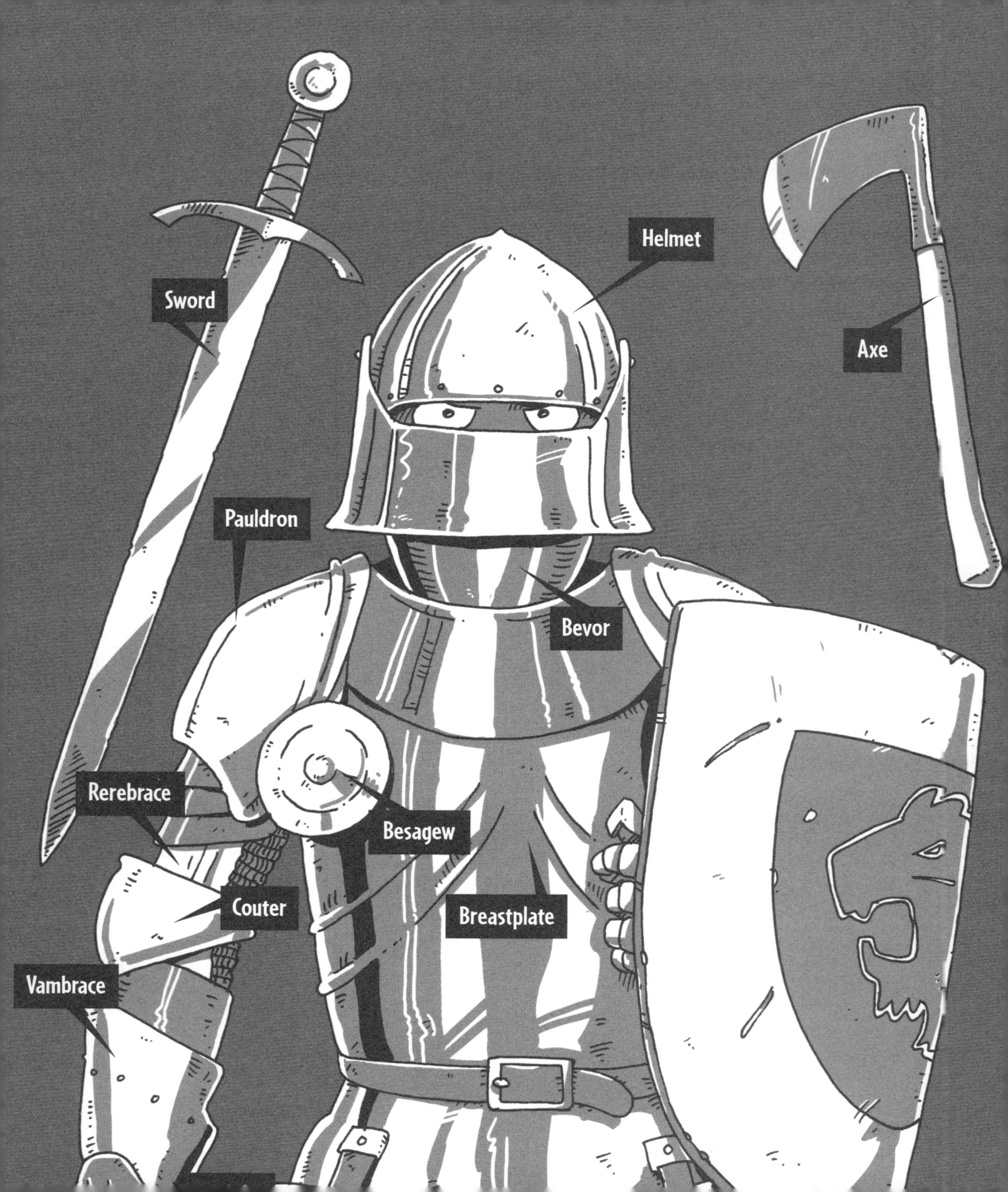
Sword
Helmet
Axe
Pauldron
Bevor
Rerebrace
Besagew
Couter
Breastplate
Vambrace

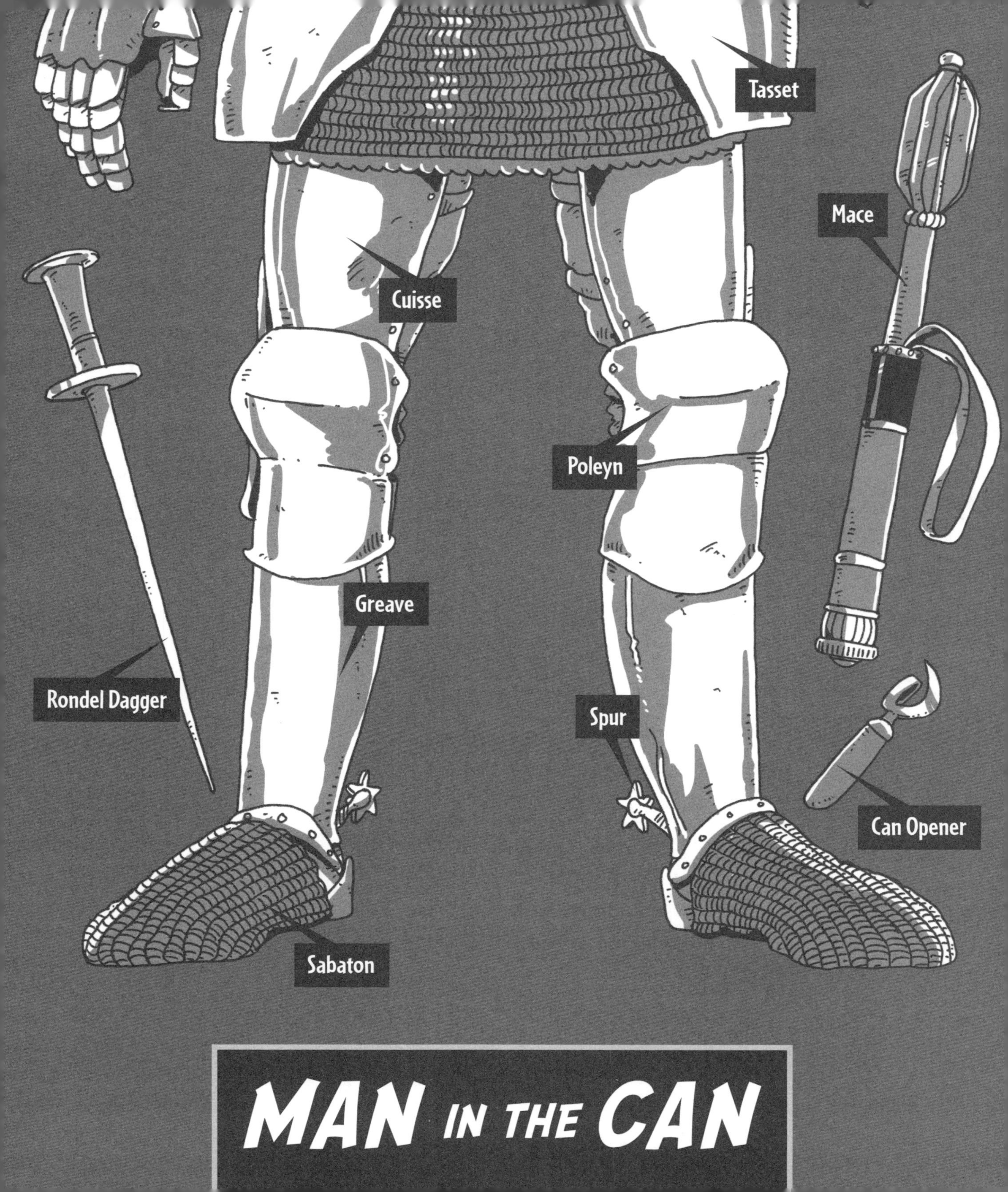
Tasset
Mace
Cuisse
Poleyn
Greave
Rondel Dagger
Spur
Can Opener
Sabaton
MAN IN THE CAN

WHICH KNIGHT IS WITCH?

FRANCE, 1428

BY 1430 IT WAS FOUL TO BE FRENCH. THE OLD KING CHARLES VI WAS MAD AND NOT FIT TO RULE. HIS SON, PRINCE CHARLES, WAS A BIT OF A WIMP AND NOT READY TO FIGHT THE ENGLISH INVADERS. MILLIONS OF FRENCH HAD BEEN KILLED OFF BY THE BLACK DEATH. IT ALL LOOKED PRETTY HOPELESS. THEN ALONG CAME A GIRL CALLED JOAN.

THEN, ONE DAY, JOAN SAID SHE HAD A MESSAGE FROM GOD...
I HEARD BEAUTIFUL VOICES. SAINT MICHAEL, SAINT CATHERINE, AND SAINT MARGARET
SHE'S A SAINT!
SHE'S A SKIVER... WHO'S LOOKING AFTER THE SHEEP?
JOAN WENT TO THE LORD WHO LIVED NEAR THE VILLAGE AND TOLD HER STORY...
LORD ROBERT, THE ANGELS TOLD ME TO DRIVE OUT THE ENGLISH AND BRING THE PRINCE TO REIMS TO BE CROWNED
GO BACK TO YOUR SHEEP, YOU SOFT-BRAINED SHEPHERD!
BUT, MY LORD, PRINCE CHARLES NEEDS MY HELP... HE HAS SUFFERED A TERRIBLE DEFEAT AT ORLÉANS
THAT'S A LIE. THE ENGLISH WILL NEVER CAPTURE ORLÉANS

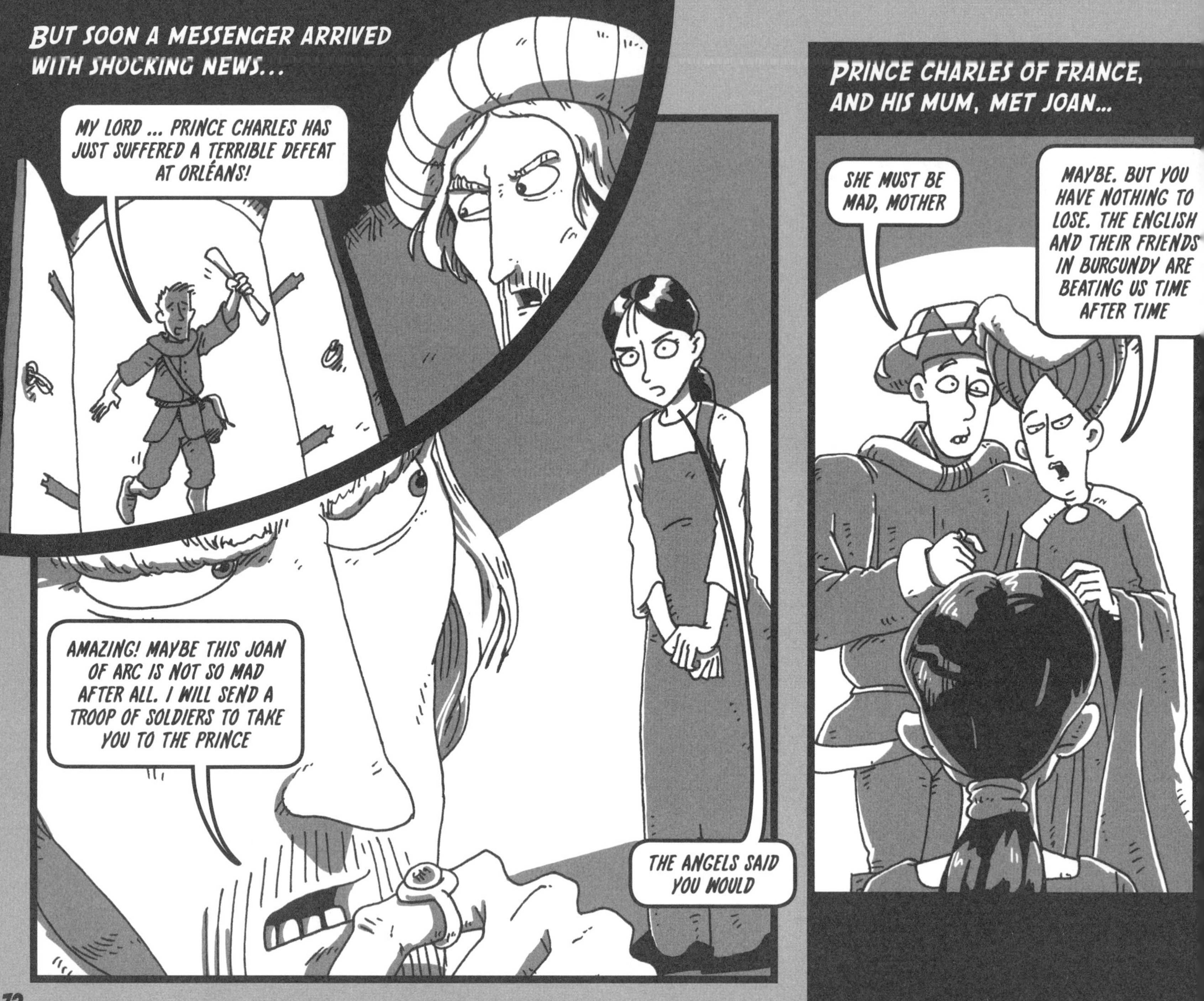
BUT SOON A MESSENGER ARRIVED WITH SHOCKING NEWS...
MY LORD ... PRINCE CHARLES HAS JUST SUFFERED A TERRIBLE DEFEAT AT ORLÉANS!
AMAZING! MAYBE THIS JOAN OF ARC IS NOT SO MAD AFTER ALL. I WILL SEND A TROOP OF SOLDIERS TO TAKE YOU TO THE PRINCE
THE ANGELS SAID YOU WOULD
PRINCE CHARLES OF FRANCE, AND HIS MUM, MET JOAN...
SHE MUST BE MAD, MOTHER
MAYBE. BUT YOU HAVE NOTHING TO LOSE. THE ENGLISH AND THEIR FRIENDS IN BURGUNDY ARE BEATING US TIME AFTER TIME

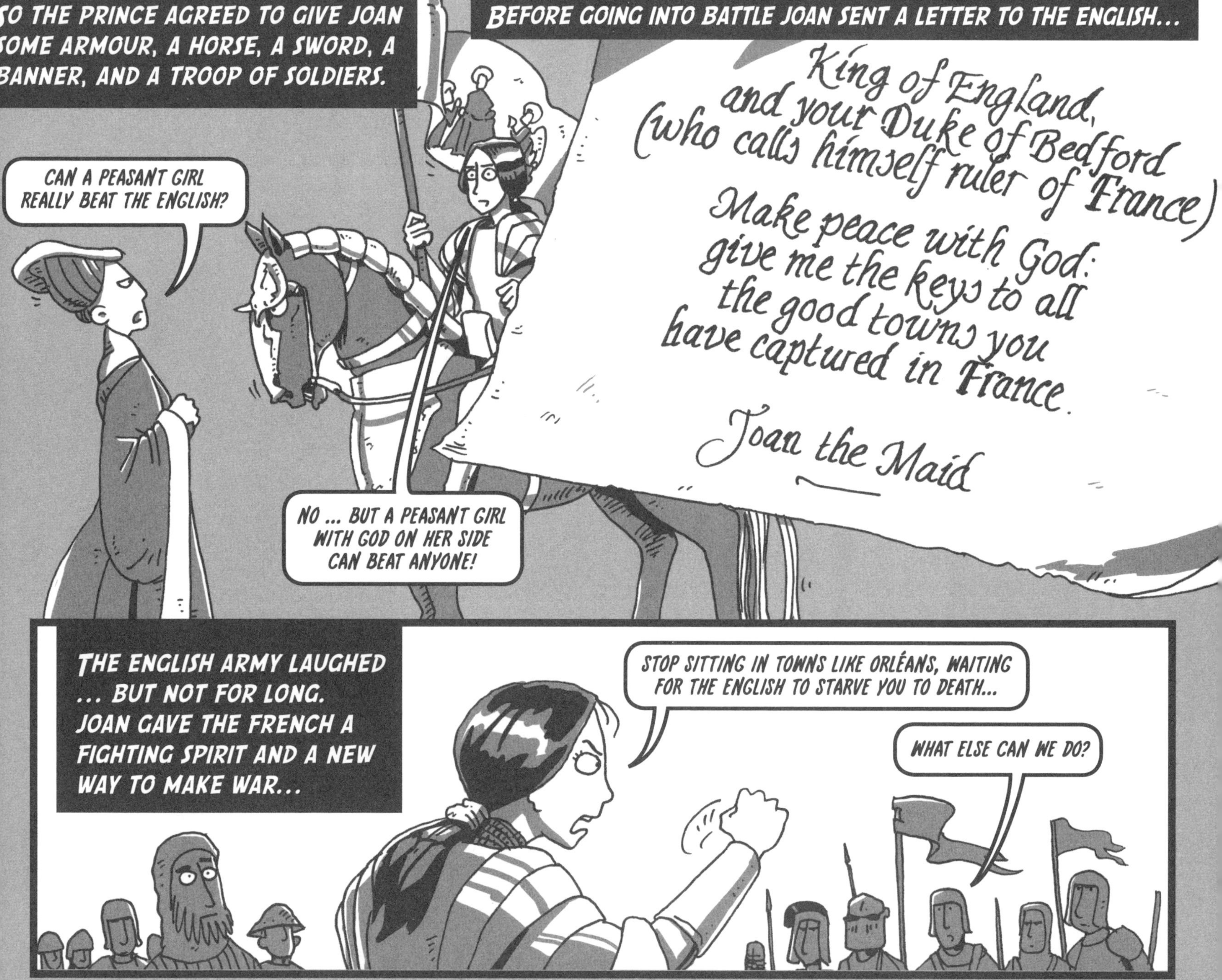
SO THE PRINCE AGREED TO GIVE JOAN SOME ARMOUR, A HORSE, A SWORD, A BANNER, AND A TROOP OF SOLDIERS.
CAN A PEASANT GIRL REALLY BEAT THE ENGLISH?
NO ... BUT A PEASANT GIRL WITH GOD ON HER SIDE CAN BEAT ANYONE!
BEFORE GOING INTO BATTLE JOAN SENT A LETTER TO THE ENGLISH...
King of England, and your Duke of Bedford (who calls himself ruler of France)
Make peace with God: give me the keys to all the good towns you have captured in France.
Joan the Maid
THE ENGLISH ARMY LAUGHED ... BUT NOT FOR LONG. JOAN GAVE THE FRENCH A FIGHTING SPIRIT AND A NEW WAY TO MAKE WAR...
STOP SITTING IN TOWNS LIKE ORLÉANS, WAITING FOR THE ENGLISH TO STARVE YOU TO DEATH...
WHAT ELSE CAN WE DO?

GO OUT AND FIGHT THEM. ATTACK. GOD AND HIS ANGELS HAVE TOLD ME YOU WILL WIN
REALLY? RIGHT, LADS, LET'S GO AND BATTER BEDFORD AND BEAT UP THE BOYS FROM BURGUNDY!
OOORAY!

THE MAYOR LOCKED THE GATES OF ORLÉANS TO STOP HER ATTACKING THE ENGLISH FORT OUTSIDE THE CITY WALLS. BUT JOAN SPOKE TO THE PEOPLE OF THE CITY...

DO WE WANT THE MAYOR TO UNLOCK THE GATES AND LET US FIGHT THE EVIL ENGLISH?
YES! OUI!
YES OUI DO!

WITH THE HELP OF COMMON SOLDIERS AND JUST ONE CAPTAIN, SHE WON. THEN THE REST OF THE FRENCH KNIGHTS JOINED HER. THE FRENCH WON BATTLE AFTER BATTLE. JOAN DIDN'T DO ANY KILLING HERSELF BUT SHE FACED THE SAME DANGERS. AT JARGEAU SHE CLIMBED THE LADDERS ON THE TOWN WALLS...

LOOK OUT!

JOAN WAS HIT BY A STONE CANNONBALL ON THE HELMET, BUT SURVIVED...

STONE OF ARC

JOAN'S ARMY CAPTURED THE CITY OF REIMS SO PRINCE CHARLES COULD BE CROWNED KING OF FRANCE IN THE CATHEDRAL.

BUT THE WAR GOES ON UNTIL WE HAVE DRIVEN THE ENGLISH OUT OF FRANCE

OH, I SUPPOSE SO. I'M NOT THAT BOTHERED NOW I'M KING

BUT IN 1430 JOAN WAS CAPTURED BY BURGUNDY SOLDIERS ON THE BATTLEFIELD. AS YOU KNOW, KNIGHTS WERE SOLD TO THEIR FAMILY FOR A RANSOM. BUT JOAN'S FAMILY WERE POOR...
HOW MUCH? WE'D HAVE TO SELL THE FARM AND ALL OUR SHEEP FOR SLAUGHTER FOR A DAUGHTER
WE'D BE RUINED
AND WE'D BE PRETTY RUINED TOO

JOAN TRIED TO ESCAPE MANY TIMES... ONCE SHE JUMPED FROM A 20-METRE TOWER - BUT IN THE END SHE WAS HANDED OVER TO THE ENGLISH.

I AM A PRISONER OF WAR. YOU CANNOT EXECUTE ME

CURSES. BY THE RULES OF CHIVALRY SHE'S RIGHT

EXCUSE ME, SIR, BUT SHE IS A WOMAN DRESSED IN A MAN'S CLOTHES. THE LAW SAYS THAT MAKES HER A WITCH

BY GOD, YOU'RE RIGHT! WE CAN'T EXECUTE A KNIGHT ... BUT WE CAN EXECUTE A WITCH

THAT'S CHEATING

SO JOAN WAS TREATED AS A WITCH, NOT A KNIGHT, TAKEN OUT AND BURNED AT THE STAKE.

JOAN OF ARC TO JOAN OF ASH

Joan died a cruel death. Her charred body was burned three times till there was nothing but ash. The ash was scattered on the river. But killing her didn't help the English much. Joan the knight had broken the English power and they never got it back. In the end Prince Charles drove them out to end the Hundred Years War. The knights needed to find new wars to fight.

COUGH
COUGH

JOLLY JOUSTING

ARROWS AND CANNONBALLS HAD MADE KNIGHTS IN ARMOUR FAIRLY USELESS. BUT THOSE POSH LORDS STILL WANTED TO DRESS IN SHINY ARMOUR AND SHOW OFF THEIR FIGHTING SKILLS. THE OLD MÊLÉES HAD BEEN FUN, BUT THEIR LOVELY LADIES COULDN'T WATCH A BATTLE THAT WAS SPREAD OUT OVER MILES. SO KNIGHTS CAME UP WITH 'JOUSTING' - PUNCH-UPS IN A PLACE THE SIZE OF A FOOTBALL PITCH.

OOOOH, I DO LOVE WATCHING A MAN IN A CAN WITH A LANCE TRYING TO KNOCK ANOTHER MAN IN A CAN OFF HIS HORSE. IT'S GOOD SPORT AND NO ONE GETS HURT
NOT TRUE ... THAT BIT ABO NO ONE GETTING HURT
IN A 1216 TOURNAMENT THE FRENCH KNIGHTS FOUGHT A FRIENDLY AGAINST THE ENGLISH KNIGHTS USING PADDED JACKETS INSTEAD OF ARMOUR AND LIGHT LANCES INSTEAD OF BATTLE LANCES. BUT ENGLISH BARON GEOFFREY DE MANDEVILLE WAS STILL KILLED ... IN A FRIENDLY WAY!
I AM... 'OW YOU SAY... REALLY VERY SORRY, OLD BEAN

THE WONDERFUL THING IS WOMEN CAN GO AND WATCH THEIR LOVER (OR THEIR FAVOURITE KNIGHT) AS HE JOUSTS
YEAH, AND THE UN-WONDERFUL THING IS A WOMAN CAN ALSO BE THE PRIZE! LOOK AT THAT GERMAN KNIGHT WALTMANN VON SETENSTETE
SEE ZIS LOVERLY GIRL? IF ANY KNIGHT COULD BEAT ME THEN ZEE WINNER GETS MY ARMOUR AND MY WEAPONS ... AND ZEE YOUNG WOMAN!
I'LL TELL YOU SOMETHING ELSE I LIKE ABOUT JOUSTS. WINNERS WERE LOSERS AND LOSERS WERE WINNERS. HERE'S HOW: THE MORE TIMES YOU ARE KNOCKED OFF YOUR HORSE AND CLIMB BACK ON, THE BRAVER YOU ARE. SO IF YOU ARE KNOCKED OFF TEN TIMES AND GET BACK ON YOU ARE INCREDIBLY BRAVE
AND IF YOU LAND ON YOUR HEAD YOU ARE DEAD BRAVE
KNIGHTS CAME FROM FAR AND WIDE BUT LUCKILY SETENSTETE BEAT THEM ALL

MIND YOU, MY LORD FITZWILLY IS HARDLY EVER KNOCKED OUT OF HIS SADDLE
MAINLY 'COS HE CHEATS
HE'S ONE OF THOSE KNIGHTS WHO HAS HIS ARMOUR MADE SO IT CAN BE SCREWED ONTO HIS SADDLE!
HE HAS NEVER BEEN CAUGHT CHEATING ... YET
I'VE SEEN ALL THE TRICKS OVER THE YEARS. THE LANCES ARE SUPPOSED TO BE BLUNT... LORD FITZWILLY SOMETIMES SNEAKS A SHARP ONE INTO THE FIGHT
HE'S NEVER BEEN CAUGHT DOING TH

THAT CAN BE DEADLY. IN 1290 DUKE LUDWIG OF BAVARIA DIED WHEN A SHARP LANCE WENT CLEAN THROUGH HIS THROAT ARMOUR
HA! HA! HA! WHAT A PAIN IN THE NECK FOR LUDWIG!
THEY ARE ALL AT IT. BOHEMIAN KNIGHTS SED A LANCE THAT WAS LONGER AND THICKER HAN EVERYONE ELSE'S! BY 1310 THEY WERE UNBEATABLE
EVERYONE REFUSED TO FIGHT THEM ... SO THEY HAD TO FIGHT EACH OTHER INSTEAD!
THEY MADE NEW RULES TO PUT A STOP TO THAT
IN THESE NEW TOURNAMENTS YOU SCORE POINTS BY BREAKING THE TIP OF YOUR LANCE AGAINST YOUR OPPONENT'S SHIELD AS YOU CHARGE TOWARDS ONE ANOTHER. THE KNIGHT BREAKING THE MOST LANCES IS DECLARED THE WINNER
CERRUNCH!

WHAT DOES CHEATING FITZWILLY DO?
HAS HIS LANCE MADE WITH A TIP AS FRAIL AS A GLASS BUTTERFLY AND THEY BREAK EVERY TIME! WHAT A CLEVER BOY
I'VE SEEN HIM HAVE AN ENEMY BEATEN UP ON HIS WAY TO THE TOURNAMENT. FITZWILLY HIRED A GANG OF SQUIRES WITH WOODEN CLUBS TO JUMP ON A RIVAL ON THE ROAD
YES, WITH A FEW BROKEN RIBS, LEGS AND A BROKEN HEAD THEY DON'T FIGHT NEARLY SO WELL
HAVE A LOOK AT HIS RIGHT GLOVE ... GAUNTLET THEY CALL IT
IT'S BEEN SPECIALL MADE FOR MY LORI

SPECIALLY MADE SO IT LOCKS
SELF AROUND A LANCE AND KEEPS
STEADY. IT'S AGAINST THE RULES
ONLY IF YOU ARE CAUGHT
BOSH
OOOOH! HE'S BEEN KNOCKED OFF HIS HORSE. IT'S A FOOT FIGHT WITH AXES. MY LORD'S GOOD AT THAT
HEH! HEH! SHAME HE'S UP AGAINST LORD RAGWORT ... AN EVEN BIGGER CHEAT
HAT'S RIGHT ... WATCH THIS... I DROPS ME AXE AND RUSHES AT ME ENEMY
AS HE RAISES HIS AXE TO STRIKE, I DRAWS ME DAGGER
AND STABS HIM UNDER THE ARM
OH, I SAY, OLD CHAP. YOU'VE OUT-CHEATED ME

WHAT DO I WATCH NOW?
WATCH ONE OF THE OTHER TOURNAMENT SPORTS LIKE CASTING THE STONE ... IN FACT WATCH OUT FOR THE STONE...
BONK!!
IN DAYS OF OLD WHEN KNIGHTS WERE BOLD...
I FEEL A LITTLE BOULDER!

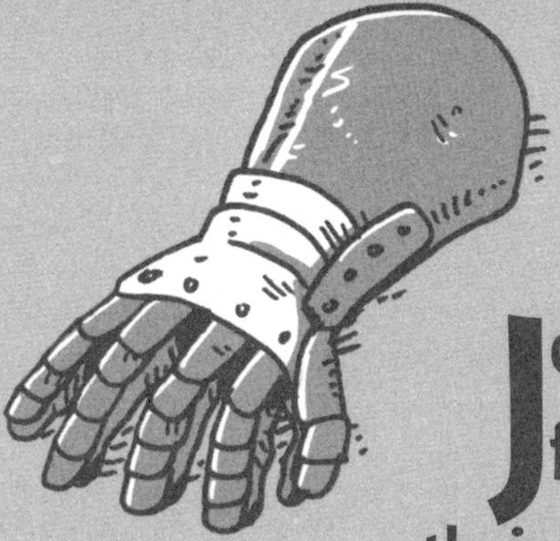

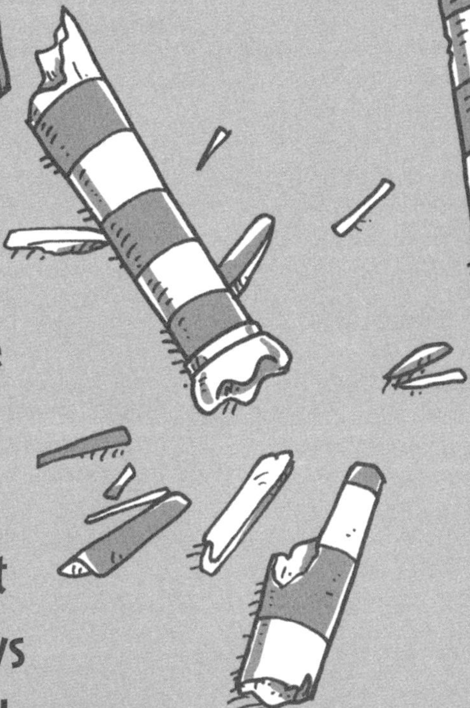

Jousting was for knights and their posh friends. The peasants (like you and me) could go and watch the fighting knights but we wouldn't get a seat in the stands. We could always crawl UNDER the stand ... but this could be dangerous when a stand collapsed. (And they sometimes did.) In Germany peasants held their own village jousts and tried to copy the knights. The knights hated these peasant tournaments and tried to stop them ... but that probably made them even more fun for the poor people in the villages!

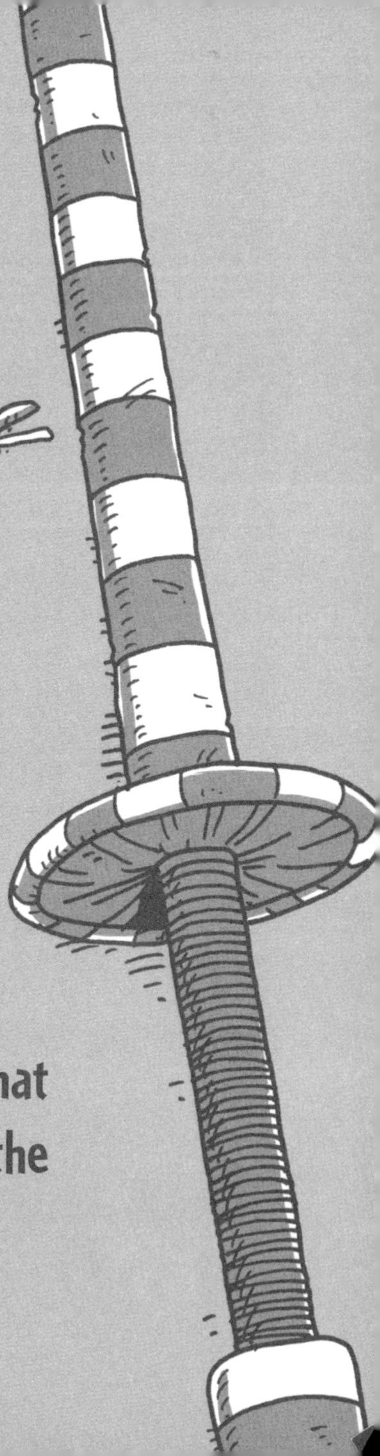

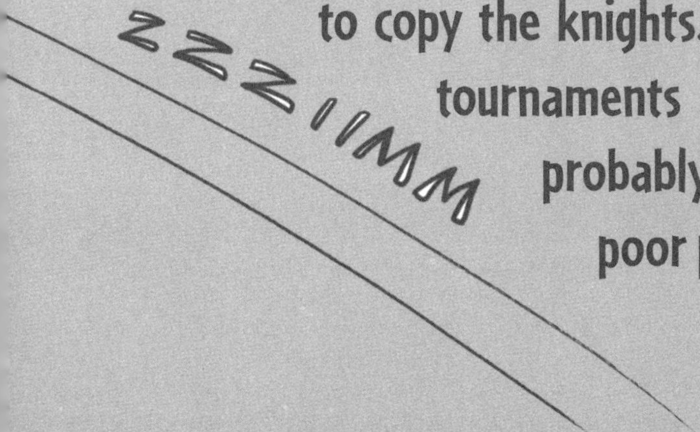

JUST JOUSTING
DONK

STOPPING THE KNIGHT

A MAN IN ARMOUR ON A HORSE WITH ARMOUR IS AS HEAVY AS YOUR FAMILY CAR. PUT A WEAPON IN HIS HAND AND WATCH HIM CHARGING TOWARDS YOU. HE WILL FLATTEN YOU. STEP ASIDE AND HE WILL USE HIS WEAPONS TO SLASH YOU AND MASH YOU. FOR HUNDREDS OF YEARS SOLDIERS LOOKED FOR WAYS TO STOP THE CHARGING KNIGHT. HERE ARE TOP TEN USEFUL TIPS IN CASE YOU MEET A HORSE-POWERED HORROR ON YOUR WAY TO THE SHOPS...

TOP TIP 1: GET YOURSELF A HORSE AND ARMOUR. IN THE 1100S, DURING THE CRUSADES, GEOFFREY OF BOUILLON WAS CHALLENGED TO A DUEL BY A TURKISH KNIGHT. THEY RODE AT EACH OTHER AND GEOFF USED HIS HUGE SWORD TO CHOP THROUGH THE TURK'S WAIST. THE TOP HALF OF THE TURK 'LAY PANTING ON THE GROUND' WHILE THE BOTTOM HALF WENT OFF AT FULL SPEED ON THE HORSE

COME BACK! IT'S ONLY A FLESH WOUND!

TOP TIP 2: CREEP UP ON YOUR ENEMY'S TENT AT NIGHT. BATTER HIM IN HIS SLEEP...

BOSH

OOF!

OW!

BASH

THUMP

BOCK

WHUMP

...BUT BE CAREFUL. SOME CRUSADERS TRIED THIS IN 1291. THEY CREPT UP ON A TURK CAMP. A CRUSADER TRIPPED OVER A TENT ROPE, FELL INTO A TURKISH TOILET PIT AND DROWNED
THAT GAVE REAL TURKISH DELIGHT
YOU CAN'T AFFORD A HORSE? TOP TIP 3: STICK A HOOK ON A LONG POLE. IN 1315 SWISS FOOT SOLDIERS USE LONG-HANDLED HOOKED KNIVES, CALLED HALBERDS, TO PULL DOWN AND BUTCHER CHARGING KNIGHTS ON HORSEBACK
SQUAT
I'M GUTTED
TOP TIP 4: THREATEN HIS KIDS. IN ENGLAND IN THE 1100S YOUNG WILLIAM MARSHALL WAS CAPTURED BY KING STEPHEN. THE KING THREATENED TO THROW YOUNG WILLIAM OVER HIS FATHER'S CASTLE WALLS WITH A GIANT CATAPULT IF DAD DIDN'T SURRENDER. HIS FATHER DIDN'T SURRENDER – WILLIAM LIVED. BUT THIS TRICK SOMETIMES WORKED
BET YOU DON'T

TOP TIP 5: CROSS A RIVER AND WAIT FOR YOUR ENEMY TO FOLLOW. ATTACK HIM AS HE PLODS THROUGH MUDDY WATER. IT MAKES HIM PANIC
THE SCOTS DID THIS AT STIRLING BRIDGE IN 1297. THE ENGLISH HORSES STRUGGLED THROUGH THE MUD. THE SCOTTISH FOOT SOLDIERS RAN DOWN THE HILL AND USED LONG SPEARS TO KNOCK THEIR ENGLISH ENEMIES OFF THEIR HORSES
ENGLISH COMMANDER, HUGH DE CRESSINGHAM, SENT THE REST OF HIS KNIGHTS TO CHARGE OVER THE BRIDGE
THE BRIDGE COLLAPSED. HUGH WAS CAPTURED AND KILLED. A REPORT SAID...
The Scottish leader, William Wallace, took a broad strip of Cressingham's skin from head to the heel, and made a new belt for his sword.

TOP TIP 6: STAND YOUR TROOPS IN A LINE WITH LONG SPEARS POINTING OUT. THE KNIGHTS RUN INTO A WALL OF SPIKES

BUT ... WHEN A SCOTTISH ARMY TRIED THIS AT FALKIRK IN 1298 THE BLOCK OF SPEARMEN MADE A NICE EASY TARGET FOR ENGLISH ARCHERS. AS A WRITER SAID...

The Scottish bodies covered the ground as thick as the snow in winter.

SNOW JOKE, EH?

TOP TIP 7: GET A BOW AND ARROWS. MANY BATTLES, LIKE CRÉCY, WERE DECIDED BY THE ARCHERS AND NOT THE KNIGHTS. EACH SIDE BEGAN THE BATTLE BY FILLING THE AIR WITH ARROWS. EVERY ARCHER TRIED TO KEEP SIX ARROWS IN THE AIR AT A TIME

HMM... FEELS LIKE RAIN?

ONE WAY OF FIRING QUICKLY WAS TO HAVE THE ARROWS STUCK IN THE GROUND, POINTS DOWN. OF COURSE THE ARROW POINTS PICKED UP DIRT THIS WAY. IF AN ENEMY SURVIVED AN ARROW WOUND THEN HE COULD DIE OF BLOOD POISONING A FEW DAYS LATER
NO PROBLEM. I'LL BE FINE
THE ARCHERS USED 'FLIGHT ARROWS' FIRST. THEY HAD LONG SHAFTS AND TRAVELLED OVER 200 METRES. THEN AS THE ENEMY DREW CLOSER THEY USED 'SHEAF ARROWS' WHICH WERE SHORTER AND COULD 'PUNCH' A HOLE THROUGH A KNIGHT'S ARMOUR
SOME ARCHERS DIPPED THE TIPS OF THEIR ARROWS IN POISON SO EVEN A SCRATCH WOULD KILL THE ENEMY. THAT'S HOW KING RICHARD I OF ENGLAND DIED IN A CRUSADE
OOH, THAT'S SHARP!

RICHARD I WAS RIDING AROUND A CASTLE HE WAS PLANNING TO CAPTURE. BERTRAM DE GURDIN WAS ONE OF THE DEFENDERS. WEAPONS WERE SO SHORT THAT BERTRAM WAS USING A FRYING PAN FOR A SHIELD. BUT HE HAD A CROSSBOW. WHEN BERT SAW RICHARD RIDING BELOW THE CASTLE WALLS HE RAISED HIS CROSSBOW AND FIRED A BOLT. IT HIT THE ENGLISH KING IN THE NECK. THAT WASN'T ENOUGH TO KILL HIM ... BUT THE POISON WAS
URGH – A BOLT FROM THE BLUE!
TOP TIP 8: HIT THE HORSE. FOOT SOLDIERS FOUND THE EASIEST WAY TO HALT A CHARGING KNIGHT WAS TO BRING DOWN HIS HORSE. POLES WITH SHARP BLADES CALLED 'PIKES' WERE AIMED AT THE HORSE AND NOT THE RIDER
WHAT DID I EVER DO TO YOU?
ANOTHER WAY TO SPEAR THE CHARGING HORSE WAS TO DIG A PIT AND FILL IT WITH SHARP POLES. THE HORSE WOULD STUMBLE AND SPEAR ITSELF ON THEM. WITH LUCK THE KNIGHT WOULD FALL ON A STAKE TOO
OW... OW OW

TOP TIP 9: LAME THE HORSE. IN BATTLE A DEFENDING ARMY WOULD OFTEN THROW DOWN 'CALTRAPS'. THESE SPIKY METAL STARS WOULD ALWAYS LAND WITH A POINT TURNED UPWARDS. THE POINT WOULD DIG INTO THE FOOT OF A HORSE AND MAKE IT RUN WILD WITH PAIN
TOP TIP 10: GET A GUN. IN THE 1280s A MONK CALLED ROGER BACON TRIED AN OLD CHINESE RECIPE TO MAKE AN EXPLODING DUST. HE HAD DISCOVERED 'GUNPOWDER'. NOW PEOPLE COULD STUFF IT INTO BULLETS AND BOMBS AND KILL MILLIONS OF OTHERS
BOOM
DOES ANYONE ELSE SMELL BACON?
BY THE 1340s THIS GUNPOWDER WAS BEING USED IN CANNON ON THE BATTLEFIELD. CHARGING KNIGHTS COULDN'T FIGHT AGAINST CANNON ... THEY WEREN'T EVEN SAFE IN THEIR CASTLES ANY LONGER

Of course you won't meet a knight on the way to the shops ... probably. They're all gone now.

The discovery of gunpowder wasn't the end for the man in a can on a horse ... but he wouldn't be around much longer. In the Crimean War of 1854 there was a mad charge of British soldiers on horses against Russian cannon. No prizes for guessing that the cannon won. It was known as 'The Charge of the Light Brigade'. A French commander said, 'It is magnificent, but it isn't war. It is stupidity.'

From Roland the hero to 'stupid' Brits on horses. The days of knights were over.

ILLUSTRATED BY

DAVE SMITH